Roswell
Park
Memorial
Institute
Main Entrance

4

# Legacy and History of
# ROSWELL PARK
### CANCER INSTITUTE
## 1898–1998

ROSWELL
PARK
CANCER
INSTITUTE

100
YEARS

PATIENT CARE
RESEARCH
EDUCATION

5–

# Legacy and History of
# ROSWELL PARK
### CANCER INSTITUTE
## 1898–1998

By Dr. Edwin A. Mirand

THE
DONNING COMPANY
PUBLISHERS

This volume is dedicated to the doctors, scientists,
nurses, employees, trainees, Board of Trustees, Board
of Visitors, volunteers, members of the community,
legislators and governors, past and present, who have
assisted Roswell Park Cancer Institute through the years
in implementing its mission—cancer research, treatment,
and education; also to those who have been closely
associated with me at the Institute during the last five
decades. I have had the the privilege of experiencing
the many events of the Institute, enabling me to write
about its history.

Dr. Edwin A. Mirand

The Donning Company/Publishers
184 Business Park Drive, Suite 106
Virginia Beach, Virginia 23462

Steve Mull, General Manager
Rick Taylor, Project Director
Dawn V. Kofroth, Assistant General Manager
Paul C. Gualdoni Jr., Graphic Designer
Jim Casper, Imaging Artist
Teri S. Arnold, Senior Marketing Coordinator

**Library of Congress Cataloging-in-Publication Data**

Mirand, Edwin A., 1926–
    Legacy and history of Roswell Park Cancer Institute, 1898–1998 / Edwin A. Mirand.
        p.     cm.
    Includes bibliographical references and index.
    ISBN 1-57864-036-9 (hardcover : alk. paper)
    1. Roswell Park Cancer Institute—History. 2. Cancer—Research—New York (State)—History. I. Title.
RC267.M56 1998
362.1'96994'00974789—dc21                    98-18365
                                       CIP

**Printed in the United States of America**

# Contents

# Foreword

One hundred years ago Dr. Roswell Park, with Mr. Edward H. Butler, Sr., labored in earnest to establish the world's first cancer research center. Their efforts in 1897 were rewarded on April 29, 1898, when the governor of New York signed the legislation to create the New York State Pathological Laboratory of the University of Buffalo in the old Medical School Building on High Street. This facility later evolved into what is known today as Roswell Park Cancer Institute.

This publication chronicles the challenges and the achievements of the Institute during its one hundred years through photographs and narrative. It depicts the efforts of so many who kept the Institute alive through good times and bad. Also, it demonstrates the unfaltering commitment of the Institute staff to meet the community's changing health care needs as developments in cancer research and health policies occurred.

In the second century of our existence, our rich history and bright future offer all of us at the Institute the opportunities to rededicate ourselves to our mission—research, treatment, and education in cancer. We expect to meet all of the challenges and opportunities that lie ahead.

I welcome the opportunity to lead the world's first cancer research institute into the second century with great enthusiasm and pride.

Dr. David C. Hohn
President and Chief Executive Officer

# Acknowledgments

I would like to thank particularly Mr. Kevin Craig
and Mrs. Colleen Karuza for their generous time
given me in providing materials and in making
many changes that I would execute along the way
in assembling this history. I am exceedingly grateful, too, to my secretaries, Ms. Linda Beverage
and Ms. Karen Cooper, for clerical assistance,
and to the Medical Photography Department,
particularly Mr. Joseph Eberle, Ms. Kathy Nasca,
and Mr. Steve Barnhart, for processing the photographs; to Dr. Joel Huberman for assistance
in writing the "Heritage of Carl and Gerty Cori
and Roswell Park Cancer Institute"; and to Cindy
Eller for her support. Lastly, my sincere thanks
and appreciation are extended to Dr. David C.
Hohn for his support and for recognizing the
need to write this history on the occasion of
our hundredth anniversary.

Dr. Edwin A. Mirand

# Introduction

## That all may know you.

"That all may know you" are meaningful words to relate a brief sketch of the life of Roswell Park Cancer Institute, at times a great story of faith in a mission, of courage, and of imagination. In that it is a legacy and history of the Institute, herein are the principal acts, events, and vicissitudes which have made the Institute what it is today. In that history, persons and personalities have of necessity to be kept at the irreducible minimum. There are literally hundreds who are unnamed, but who have contributed so much to the life of Roswell Park Cancer Institute. Without them, the Institute would not be what it is today. Indeed, without them, it is doubtful if the Institute would even be!

Therefore, due to the exigencies of time and space, to the many who will remain unknown, unhonored, and unsung, save in the minds and hearts of those who know, accept my apology. I hope the reader is assured that although the faces may be missing from pictures, the names from print, their character and deeds are nonetheless forever enshrined in the hearts of those who know them firsthand. I dedicate this effort to all who contributed so conscientiously to make Roswell Park Cancer Institute what it was, what it is, and what it will be in the next millennium—

## *Ut Omnes Te Cognoscant.*

DR. EDWIN A. MIRAND
Vice President and Dean Emeritus
Senior Advisor to the President and CEO

# Prologue

Roswell Park Cancer Institute, the New York State Health Department's cancer research and treatment center, is a unique facility. Entering the twenty-first century and its second century with a newly constructed and renovated campus, Roswell Park Cancer Institute is an impressive landmark near downtown Buffalo, New York. But, it is much more than bricks, mortar, and glass. It is the embodiment of the philosophy of Dr. Roswell Park who, shortly before the turn of the century, had become deeply concerned at the lack of an organized national and international effort to investigate the nature of cancer in a multidisciplinary manner as a means to improve treatment. This effort to attack the cancer problem, he felt, must use all scientific disciplines in a designated institutional setting. His multidisciplinary approach insisted on a combination of laboratory discoveries, patient care, and professional and public education—the blueprint for the modern cancer center.

Dr. Park stated, *Only* [through] *a deliberate, well-planned, combined attack from various directions by means fitted for such work could real advances be made and* [further] *the relationship of laboratory work, clinical study and education must be closely associated.* This was a revolutionary approach to the investigation of cancer since prior to this (if cancer research was conducted at all) it was conducted in a single disciplinary manner and in an ad hoc fashion. A partisan, single disciplinary view was held by practically every investigator.

**0-1.**
Dr. Roswell Park, distinguished surgeon and professor of surgery at University of Buffalo School of Medicine, founded RPCI in 1898.

The lack of an organized national and international effort to study cancer was not surprising. Although considered a baffling medical mystery, cancer was not one of the most feared and fatal diseases of the day. Pneumonia and influenza, tuberculosis, diarrhea enteritis, heart disease, and others had that role at that time. These diseases, other than heart, have been almost eliminated as causes of death in the United States. However, at the turn of the century, Dr. Park urged the New York State government to accept cancer as a public health problem on the rise worldwide, which he predicted would be one of the major causes of death in the twentieth century. He also influenced other states and countries (England, Germany, Russia, France, Japan) to accept cancer as a public health problem. Dr. Park's recognition of cancer's complexity and longevity has been justified. Today, it ranks second only to heart disease as the leading cause of death from disease in the United States.

The concept of developing a cancer research laboratory in three small rooms in the University of Buffalo School of Medicine set Dr. Park apart as a pioneer. But, this role transcended medical research for Dr. Park. History records that he also pioneered the modern day structure of government funding of, and community support for, medical research on specific diseases. Dr. Park believed it was the proper function of government to support biomedical research, particularly cancer. History also records that his philosophical offspring include not only Roswell Park Cancer Institute, but the network of National Cancer Institute–designated comprehensive cancer centers developed since the passage of the National Cancer Act in 1971.

Here's how the story unfolded and continues to unfold—always dependent upon good, cooperative relationships with the Governor's office, New York State legislators, the New York State Department of Health, the community, and staff support. You will witness this from Dr. Roswell Park's administration to Dr. David C. Hohn's administration.

**Off to Albany!**
Roswell Park Cancer Institute was organized in 1898, largely through the untiring efforts and imagination of Dr. Roswell Park, a distinguished surgeon who was Professor of Surgery at the University of Buffalo School of Medicine, and Edward H. Butler, Sr., founder and publisher of the BUFFALO EVENING NEWS. Dr. Park saw the need for a cancer research laboratory, but knew he would need help in obtaining funds from the community and government to make it a reality. This approach to supporting cancer research was unprecedented, and Mr. Butler was the obvious person for Dr. Park to approach for assistance. The publisher was an aggressive, community-minded newspaperman who saw the merit of Dr. Park's proposal and who, more importantly, had many prominent and influential friends in the Albany legislature as well as in the Buffalo area.

0-2.
Mr. Edward H. Butler, Sr., founder and publisher of the BUFFALO EVENING NEWS, assisted Dr. Park in getting legislative effort to establish RPCI by applying political pressure on legislators and Governor F. S. Black.

Dr. Park and Mr. Butler actually began their work on February 26, 1897, in Albany. They met with Governor Frank S. Black, and Dr. Park addressed the New York State legislature's Ways and Means Committee. Their request was that the State provide a grant of $10,000 to establish a cancer laboratory within the University of Buffalo School of Medicine. Then, on March 30, 1897, Dr. Park met with Senator O. Ellsworth who had misgivings about the State engaging in cancer investigation. Mr. Butler had the political acumen and influence to assure passage of a bill by the legislature providing for the grant, but the bill was vetoed by Governor Black. The governor explained that he could not approve a proposed policy that required the State to engage in investigating the causes of various diseases. This, he said, *was a function that the interest of the people and the skills of physicians could be depended upon to undertake.*

DR. ROSWELL PARK.
510 DELAWARE AVENUE.
HOURS 8 TO 10, 1:30 TO 2:30
TELEPHONE, TUPPER 101.

BUFFALO, March, 30th, 1897.

Hon. Frank W. Higgins,

Albany, N. Y.

My Dear Sir:—

I had quite an interview on Saturday with Senator Ellsworth whose interest in the Cancer Investigation I trust I have aroused, and from whom I learned that the amount asked for i.e. $15,000, had been cut in halves by his committee before being included in the Supply Bill. I regretted very deeply to learn this, because if we equip a laboratory and library for this work as we would wish to do there would be not enough left to command the services of men such as we would wish to engage. I think you will agree with me in this matter and as to the wisdom of restoring the sum to the original amount in the Conference Committee. This would give us the use of so much as might be necessary without either crippling us or compelling us to use it all.

Senator Ellsworth. I think was somewhat uncertain as to the wisdom of the State engaging in any such investigation, but I did my best to convince him that if we are ever going to learn what we have to deal with it can only be by means of collective investigation with public aid, no private means ever having been put at disposal for this purpose, anywhere in the world, that I know of.

May I add to this that I am quite willing to go Albany again and talk all this to anyone to whom it would be wise to say it, if I may only receive advice from you or from him so to do.

Thanking you again for your continued interest in the matter,

I am,

Most sincerely yours,

Roswell Park.

**0-5.**
Letter of Dr. Park—
March 30, 1897.

DR. ROSWELL PARK.
510 DELAWARE AVENUE.
HOURS 8 TO 10, 1:30 TO 2:30
TELEPHONE, TUPPER 101.

BUFFALO, Feb. 26th, 1897.

Hon. Frank W. Higgins,

Albany, N. Y.

My Dear Sir:—

I was in Albany Wednesday last, where I appeared before the Ways & Means Committee, through the courtesy of Mr Nixon their chairman; I spoke my little piece, was very kindly received, aroused some interest in the matter, and feel pretty sure that they will insert the desired item in the Supply Bill. After that interview Mr Nixon took me down to see the Governor who, you know, was non-committal. Twice I went over to the Senate Chamber trying to find you, each time was told you were in the building but nobody knew where. I left a card with some clerk in the Finance Committee rooms who promised to see that you got it, but I fear he did not keep his promise. I also had a casual meeting with Senator Mullen, but did not have time to explain matters to him. His brother-in-law Mr Brown, of this city, has promised me to explain the matter to him when he sees him next week.

I left Albany at four o'clock or should certainly have availed myself of any chance to see you; if for no other reason certainly to thank you for courtesies already extended.

Trusting that everything may go well, I am,

Very sincerely yours,

Roswell Park.

**0-4.**
Letter of Dr. Park—
February 26, 1897.

11

0-6.
Copy of legislative
origin of Roswell Park
Cancer Institute

**Chap. 606.**

AN ACT* making appropriations for certain expenses of government and supplying deficiencies in former appropriations.

Became a law April 29, 1898, with the approval of the Governor. Passed by a two-thirds vote.

The People of the State of New York, represented in Senate and Assembly, do enact as follows:

Payments by treasurer. Section 1. The treasurer shall pay, on the warrant of the comptroller, from the several funds specified, to the persons, and for the objects indicated in this act, the amounts named, or such parts of those amounts as shall be sufficient to accomplish, in full, the purposes designated by the appropriations, but no warrants, shall be issued, except in cases of salaries, until the amounts claimed shall have been audited and allowed by the comptroller, who is hereby authorized to determine the same. The persons demanding payment shall present to him a detailed statement, in items, verified by affidavit; and if the account shall be for services, it must show when, where and under what authority they were rendered; if for expenditures, when, where and may be necessary, to be paid upon the rendering of the accounts duly certified and after due audit by the comptroller

Swart Murphy, stenographer to the committee on taxation and retrenchment, four hundred and twenty-five dollars.

For Caroline Austin Sickels, widow of the late Hiram E. Sickels, reporter of the court of appeals, who died July four, eighteen hundred and ninety-five, so much of the annual compensation of said reporter for the year eighteen hundred and ninety-five as would have been earned by him had he continued to live until the close of that year, the sum of two thousand four hundred and forty-five dollars and twenty cents.

The sum of fifteen thousand dollars is hereby appropriated for the expenses of the commissioners appointed by the governor to investigate the expenditure of the nine million dollar canal appropriation, or so much thereof as may be necessary.

For the faculty of the medical department of the university of Buffalo, for the equipment and maintenance of a laboratory to be devoted to an investigation into the causes, nature, mortality rate and treatment of cancer; and the salaries of officials of the same, ten thousand dollars; same to be paid upon vouchers officially signed by the director of said laboratory, or, in his absence, by the secretary and treasurer of the faculty.

For the salary of the custodian of the Grant cottage, as provided by chapter six hundred and sixty-seven of the laws of eighteen hundred and ninety-six, the sum of one thousand dollars For repairs to the Grant cottage, situate on Mount McGregor, the sum of three hundred dollars.

Early the next year, Dr. Park and Mr. Butler went to Albany again to make another attempt at obtaining a grant for a cancer laboratory. Again, the legislature passed a bill providing for the requested grant, but now Governor Black, who was up for reelection, yielded to the persuasion exerted by Dr. Park and Mr. Butler.

Governor Black signed the bill on April 29, 1898 (Chapter 606, page 1449, 1898). The legislation provided for *the equipment and maintenance of a laboratory devoted to an investigation into the causes, nature, mortality rate, and treatment of cancer.* Originally designated the New York State Pathological Laboratory of the University of Buffalo, this laboratory was the first in the world with a staff from various disciplines devoting full time to the study of cancer. It has been cited as the first historical instance in which any government took a direct, active interest in cancer research and sponsored a group attack on the disease . . . *the first laboratory ever or anywhere, created for the concerted and deliberate study of the most mysterious disease known to us, one which annually kills seven thousand of the inhabitants of this same State.*

*This laboratory is amply justified by the difficulty of the problems involved, the evidently increasing death rate from this disease, and the impossibility of studying it by purely private means. The laboratory is equipped with every possible facility for investigating the disease, both in its clinical and pathological aspects.* Dr. Roswell Park, 1898.

On October 21, 1899, an editorial in the JOURNAL OF THE AMERICAN MEDICAL ASSOCIATION stated: *So far, this country has been the only one in which there has been established a laboratory [for the] exclusive investigation of carcinoma and tumors in general. The great State of New York supports such a laboratory in Buffalo.*

Mr. Butler's successful efforts in persuading Governor Black to sign the bill providing support for Dr. Park's proposed cancer laboratory had an interesting sequel. Later that same year, Mr. Butler vigorously supported Governor Black for renomination, but the incumbent faced overwhelming odds. Political leaders nominated a candidate glorified as the hero of San Juan Hill, Colonel Theodore Roosevelt.

0-7.

**0-7.**

The University of Buffalo
School of Medicine on
High Street was the first
location of Roswell Park
Cancer Institute, known
then as the New York
State Pathological
Laboratory of the
University of Buffalo.

In 1903, during a period of fiscal stringency, Governor Benjamin B. Odell threatened to veto a bill appropriating funds for continuation of Dr. Park's cancer laboratory. Mr. Butler instructed the Albany correspondent for the BUFFALO EVENING NEWS to inform the Governor that if the bill was not approved, he would have a fight on his hands. Governor Odell did approve the bill, and there has never been any serious question about continuation of the State's cancer program since then, although there have been major fiscal hurdles from time to time.

Mr. Butler's forceful action to implement Dr. Park's proposal for the establishment of a laboratory devoted entirely to the multidisciplinary study of cancer was the publisher's foremost contribution to human welfare. This laboratory, proposed by Dr. Park and brought into existence through the aid of Mr. Butler, has evolved into Roswell Park Cancer Institute.

From its humble beginnings in three small rooms in the University of Buffalo School of Medicine, Dr. Park's laboratory has become a multimillion-dollar center that includes a new hospital and some of the most modern, best-equipped cancer research laboratories in the world.

**1-1.**
Dr. Roswell Park, the distinguished surgeon, operates at the Buffalo General Hospital across from the Gratwick Research Laboratory. (Left to right, third from left)

1904

JOHN E. OWENS
NATHANIEL P. DANDRIDGE
J. EDWIN MICHAEL
JAMES McCANN
PHINEAS S. CONNER
ROSWELL PARK
CHARLES T. PARKES
LOUIS McL. TIFFANY
THOS. J. DUNOTT
WM. H. CARMALT
THEODORE F. PREWITT
WILLIAM W. KEEN
De F. WILLARD
DAVID PRINCE
JOSEPH C. HUTCHINSON
CLAUDIUS H. MASTIN

J. EWING MEARS
JACOB R. WEIST
BERIAH A. WATSON
NICHOLAS SENN
EDWARD M. MOORE
SILAS N. BENHAM
MOSES GUNN
WM. T. BRIGGS
D. HAYES AGNEW
JOHN S. BILLINGS

**1-2.**
The most distinguished
surgeons in the
nineteenth century
accepted Dr. Roswell
Park as one of them
very early in his career.
Dr. Park, in his late
twenties, is sporting
a Bismarck beard
presumably to make
him look older among
his bearded colleagues.

As the Institute celebrates its centennial, the spirit of its remarkable founder, Dr. Roswell Park, still emanates. Dr. Park had come to Buffalo in 1883 at the age of thirty-one to become professor of surgery at the University of Buffalo Medical School and shortly thereafter surgeon at Buffalo General Hospital. He came from Chicago where he had excelled at Rush Medical College and was recognized as an ornament to the profession. He was a gifted surgeon who had pursued an outstanding career as a professor and researcher, and actively participated in cultural affairs of the community. Dr. Park received the degrees of B.A. in 1872 and M.A. in 1875 from Racine College, his medical degree from Northwestern University, 1876, an honorary M.A. from Harvard in 1895, and an honorary LL.D. from Yale in 1902. He served on many national and international boards and committees, produced an amazing number of textbooks, articles, and monographs (167 by 1914), and lectured before numerous scientific societies. His interest in tumors and his pride in his laboratory were illustrated in an address that he delivered before the American Surgical Association in New Orleans May 6, 1901. He asserted that *Buffalo was the geographical center of the American cancer district.* Dr. Park was recognized as one of the leading surgeons of his day. He was called on to supervise the care of President William McKinley, who was assassinated in Buffalo in 1901.

**1-3.**
The Gratwick Research Laboratory was built through the generous donation of Mrs. W. H. Gratwick, letter of August 28, 1900.

Nevertheless, Dr. Park's interests ranged far beyond his field. His knowledge and prodigious reading of history, classical mythology, and the humanities enabled him to write and lecture on such esoteric subjects as medico-Christian symbolism, thanatology (a term he proposed in an 1912 article in the JOURNAL OF THE AMERICAN MEDICAL ASSOCIATION), the relationship of Grecian mysteries to the foundation of Christianity, student life in the Middle Ages, and the philosophy of Giordano Bruno.

Thus, it is fitting that Dr. Park's name is perpetuated in that of the Roswell Park Cancer Institute. At the Institute, varied activities of research, diagnosis, treatment, and education range widely over the various fields of human knowledge in efforts to solve one of the most baffling mysteries of all, the cause of cancer. The philosophical, humanitarian, and scientific spirit of Dr. Park lives on, animating the work of hundreds of physicians and nurses, laboratory scientists and technicians and students who are dedicating their lives, as he did, to the betterment of mankind.

One of the medical students he taught in 1913, Dr. Oscar J. Oberkircher, an outstanding urologist from Buffalo, recalled in a letter sent to Dr. Gerald P. Murphy on April 21, 1971, how he *had the privilege of being invited to his* (Dr. Park's) *home on several occasions, where he loved to talk on medical history, of which he had great knowledge.* He was recognized by students and peers alike as a born teacher and researcher. He was among the first to acquire a knowledge of tumors and called to the attention of the country and the world the long-contested fact that cancer was steadily on the increase.

Two years after Dr. Park began his work, his research outgrew the space available at the University of Buffalo. Public-spirited citizens of Buffalo raised funds to purchase the land, and, largely through the generosity of Mrs. William Gratwick, the Gratwick Research Laboratory of the University of Buffalo was built and occupied by 1901. In proposing the construction of such a laboratory, Mrs. Gratwick's son, W. H. Gratwick wrote to Dr. Park, August 28, 1900:

> *My dear Doctor Park–*
> *My mother wishes me to say that she would consider it a privilege to assume the expenses of building a laboratory to be devoted to the investigation of cancer, such as is contemplated by you; the expenses of such an undertaking to be about $25,000.*
>
> *And she wishes me to say that one of the strong reasons influencing her decision is that the work will be under your supervision and management.*
>
> *My mother wishes to attach no conditions whatever in this matter, but she would much appreciate it if her name could be kept out of the newspapers in connection therewith, feeling averse to any publicity in the case.*
> *Yours sincerely,*
> *W. H. Gratwick*

1-5.

**1-4.**
The second location (1901) of RPCI was in the Gratwick Research Laboratory of the University of Buffalo located on High and Elm Streets.
**1-5.**
Library in the Gratwick Research Laboratory.
**1-6.**
The Director's Office in the Gratwick Research Laboratory.
**1-7.**
The animal colony facility in original Gratwick Research Laboratory to house cancer strains of mice.
**1-8.**
Our first Auditorium in the Gratwick Research Laboratory.
**1-9.**
Animal colony in Gratwick Research Laboratory in 1910 filled with live animals (picture taken from NEW YORK TIMES article of April 17, 1910).

**1-6.**

**1-7.**

**1-8.**

**1-9.**

Dr. Park received encouragement from not only friends and colleagues, but governments worldwide. There was great enthusiasm for his concept of applying a multidisciplinary research approach to the cancer problem in an institute setting. Among them was his cousin, Dr. William H. Welch of Johns Hopkins, the man credited with transforming American medical schools from the worst to the best in the world, in one generation. Another supporter was Dr. William Osler, the world-famous physician and teacher, who was a frequent visitor. Dr. Osler, to whom Dr. Park dedicated one of his books, expressed his feelings on the laboratory in a letter to Dr. Park, March 18, 1903:

**1-10.**
Dr. Osler's letter.

*THE QUESTION OF CANCER RESEARCH IN AMERICA*
  *Doctor Park,*

  *Considering the enormous and increasing importance of the subject, it is surprising how little systematic work on cancer has been undertaken in this country. So far as I know, the only Laboratory devoted to it is that organized by you and supported by the New York State Government. I was most delightfully impressed on my recent visit with the character of the researches going on in the Laboratory. Of course, it takes years to clear the ground, but there can be no question that we are on the right track at present. To successfully deal with the question requires large, expensive equipment and staff of thoroughly trained men who should devote years to the work. Only by the help of large endowments can the proper organization be maintained, and while the present equipment of Buffalo is first class, much more money is needed, and I am fully convinced that there is no problem in the preventive and rational medicine more deserving of generous endowment by men of means than that which holds out hope of discovering the origin, and through it, the successful treatment of cancer.*

*With best wishes for your work, believe me,*
  *Sincerely yours,*
  *Wm. Osler*

By the turn of the century and into the early part of the twentieth century, Dr. Park's model had gained acceptance and similar laboratories had been put into operation with government aid in Berlin, Frankfurt, Moscow, Japan, and London. In fact, several physicians were sent to Buffalo from London to consult with Dr. Park and Dr. Harvey R. Gaylord and in 1902 established the Cancer Research Fund.

During Dr. Park's career, he was president of the American Surgical Association, the Medical Society of the State of New York and the American Association for the Advancement of Science. Dr. Park was also a member of the principal medical societies in Germany, Italy, and France.

**1-11.**
Dr. Roswell Park's
portraits from
1880 to 1913.

1880

1901

1905

1909

1909

1913

**2-1.**
Dr. Harvey R. Gaylord,
the second director
of RPCI, who Dr. Park
identified quickly
as a colleague (1898).

# Chapter 2

# Before and After the First World War, Coming of Age: The Gaylord Years

**2-2.**
Later picture (1914) of Dr. Gaylord (right) talking to Dr. Charles Cary in the Solarium of the Gratwick Research Laboratory.

Dr. Park, a man of rare energy, continued to lecture, teach, write, and manage an extensive private practice in addition to carrying on ambitious research at the Laboratory. In 1904, when it became apparent that he could not, in addition, handle the Laboratory's administrative work, his collaborator, Dr. Harvey R. Gaylord, who had received his medical degree from the University of Pennsylvania in 1893 and joined Dr. Park as head of the Pathology Department and first scientific director in 1898, became the second director of the Institute.

Dr. Gaylord's association with the Institute began by happenstance. Dr. Gaylord had arranged to meet Dr. Park in Buffalo in 1898 on his way home to Saginaw, Michigan, from Europe, where he had been studying pathology under Professor Ludwig Aschoff of Germany. Dr. Park knew after their brief encounter that he wanted Dr. Gaylord to join him at the Institute. In fact, the appearance of Dr. Gaylord at this time, with his splendid European training in pathology, seemed an act of Divine Providence to Dr. Park. Fortunately for the Institute, Dr. Gaylord proved to be a dynamic successor to Dr. Park.

Dr. Park retained the position of chairman of the Board of Trustees. New York State continued to fund the operation and maintenance of the new Gratwick Research Laboratory through an annual grant of between $15,000 and $18,000. It is interesting to note that Dr. Gaylord's monthly salary in those days was $166.66, as recorded in longhand in the Institute's ledger! Dr. Gaylord's only assistant during his administration was his secretary Miss C. A. Maclay.

During those early years, the senior staff consisted of fifteen men. Dr. Park (surgeon); Dr. Gaylord (pathologist); Dr. Herbert D. Pease (clinical associate); Dr. Irving P. Lyon (clinical microscopy, epidemiologist); Dr. George H. A. Clowes (chemist, physicist); Dr. H. G. Matzinger (bacteriologist); Dr. N. W. Wilson (clinical associate); Mr. M. C. Marsh (biologist); Professor Cary N. Calkins (biologist); Dr. F. W. Baeslack (histologist); Dr. D. R. Averill (chemist); Dr. Leo Loeb (biologist); Dr. F. S. Law (photo-chemist); Dr. E. W. Jeffcoat (chemist); and Dr. F. C. Busch (clinical associate).

**2-3.**
One of fifteen early prominent senior staff members of the Institute was Dr. George H. A. Clowes, who initiated the first organized screening program to test chemicals and drugs in experimental and clinical tumors. He and Dr. Gaylord conducted the first comprehensive studies on immunologic factors of cancer.

Dr. Gaylord's major research interests were in finding an organism that caused cancer and the immunological aspects of cancer. Drs. Gaylord, Clowes, and F. W. Baeslack reported the first comprehensive studies on immunologic factors of cancer in 1904. To quote from a letter from Dr. William H. Welch, professor of surgery at Johns Hopkins Medical School, *The investigations in the Buffalo laboratory have been conducted by those who are thoroughly trained for such work and the results are already of much value and are so recognized in the medical and scientific world. The discovery there of immunity from cancer in lower animals and of rendering animals experimentally immune is perhaps the most important which has been made in this field of research.*

Drs. Gaylord, Clowes, and F. W. Baeslack also initiated the first organized screening program to test chemicals and drugs in experimental and clinical tumors. This project was carried forward for many years by Mr. Millard C. Marsh.

In a speech given by Dr. Gaylord in 1911, he said: *After three years work under the appropriations by the State, the State Cancer Laboratory came out solidly for the parasitic theory of cancer and has for ten years consistently supported this theory in face of great discouragement, until within the last year scientists are beginning to realize that this is the ultimate solution to the problem, and are willing to accord to the State Laboratory the credit of having been almost the sole supporter of this theory in the United States. Within the last six months the Rockefeller Institute has adopted the same point of view and at the International Cancer Congress in Paris the consensus of opinion in favor of the parasitic theory, and the position of the State on this question was generously recognized.*

*Studies in immunity in cancer are conceded to have originated in the State Cancer Laboratory in 1904 and today all of the institutions engaged in cancer research are working along the lines first laid down by this institution.*

Drs. Pease, Lyon, Matzinger, and Wilson made a careful, painstaking, statistical study of cancer mortality rates in New York State, particularly in Western New York. Dr. Loeb published his now classic transplantation experiments with rat sarcoma. A colony of 3,000 mice and 300 rats was maintained for research in spontaneous and transplantable tumors, and antibodies in mice recovering from experimental tumors were studied. Professor Cary N. Calkins worked on the stimulatory effects of protoplasmic substances on cell division.

To elaborate further on one of the most prominent early senior investigators leads me to Dr. George Henry Alexander Clowes (1877–1953), who married a woman from Buffalo, Edith W. Hinkel. Their three sons were born in Buffalo. One of their sons, Alexander, died of leukemia at an early age. This stimulated the efforts of Dr. Clowes to find a cure for cancer.

Before coming to Buffalo in 1901, Clowes had been advised by the renowned Professor Ehrlich of Germany, for whom he worked, that the prospects for achieving control of cancer were remote, that his scientific reputation would suffer if he spent his future life fruitlessly in pursuit of this objective, and that, therefore, a young man in the cancer field should have another line in which he could establish a sound position. This advice led Dr. Clowes to chemical and physiochemical observations and insights into the structure of biological membranes which made him a national figure in general physiology and biological chemistry.

One of his first projects at the Gratwick Research Laboratory was to establish a strain of transplanted tumors which he hoped to use as objects for chemotherapeutic tests. Almost immediately, he came upon one of the most important discoveries of his life, the spontaneous immunity to further transplants shown by rats in which a previous transplant had spontaneously regressed. The method of charting tumor size which he described in papers of 1905 and 1906 became the standard in the field for several years. Thereafter, he tried, by the methods of the day, to develop an antigen which could confer immunity to cancer growth upon a tumor-free animal.

In addition to these studies, he published on the reliability of chemical methods for cancer diagnosis of the stomach, the influence of x-rays on the metabolism of research animals, immune substances in the blood of mice spontaneously recovered from cancer, and the testing of more than 250 chemicals as possible anticancer drugs. Dr. Clowes is recognized for establishing the concept of chemotherapy and establishing the first chemotherapy program in 1904.

Dr. Clowes maintained his research at the Institute for more than a dozen years. However, his chemotherapeutic study of tumor observations created friction with some senior investigators in the Buffalo laboratory who had little attraction to the biochemical inhibitory approach to cancer research. Consequently, Dr. Clowes left the Institute in 1917 for a position at Washington, D.C., in the research division of the Chemical Warfare Service of the United States Army.

**2-4.**
Dr. George H. A. Clowes in his later years.

At the end of the war, Dr. Clowes joined the staff of Eli Lilly & Co., the pharmaceutical company in Indianapolis. There, after Dr. Frederick G. Banting and Dr. Charles H. Best had demonstrated the value of the hormone insulin in the control of diabetes at the University of Toronto in 1921, Dr. Clowes played a leading role in developing methods for the commercial manufacture and clinical use of insulin. As a result of his continuing association with the Institute, physicians in Buffalo were among the first outside of Toronto to obtain insulin for investigative and clinical use. For his efforts in insulin research, the American Diabetes Association awarded him the Banting Medal in 1947.

Dr. Clowes died in 1958, at the age of eighty-one. He received national recognition when the American Association for Cancer Research, of which he was a charter member, established the G. H. A. Clowes Memorial Lecture. The first lecture in this series was presented in 1961. The Clowes Lecture continues to be an integral part of the organization's annual meetings today. Wishing to acknowledge the work of Dr. Clowes within the Institute, Roswell Park also established an annual Clowes Lecture Series in 1973. Dr. Vincent T. DeVita, then director of the National Cancer Institute, presented the first lecture.

Between 1907 and 1910 cancer research conducted at the Gratwick Research Laboratory was beginning to have an impact nationally. The Institute staff collaborated with the famous Professor A. Borrel at Pasteur Institute; Professor Carl Olaf Jensen of Copenhagen; Madame Marie Curie of the University of Paris; Dr. Peyton Rous of Rockefeller Institute who was familiar with the work of Dr. Gaylord and colleagues on the parasitic theory of cancer; Professor Von Leyden, head of the German Society of Cancer Investigation; Professor Ludwig Aschoff of Freiburg; Professor Morau of France; Professor Ehrlich of Frankfurt; and Professor Bashford of London.

In 1907 Dr. Gaylord received many letters from foremost physicians (Dr. William H. Welch, U.S.A.; Dr. J. George Adami, Canada; Professor Aschoff, Germany; Professor C. A. Ballance, England) and scientists (Dr. A. Borrel, France) in this country and Europe; and societies (Society of Clinical Surgery, Medical Society of the State of New York) in support of his requests to the New York State legislature for continuing appropriations. The Institute was just nine years old. One such letter addressed to Senator Henry W. Hill was written by the famous physician Sir William Osler, at that time Professor of Medicine at Oxford. He wrote: *The problems connected with this terrible disease are of such importance to humanity and at the same time so complicated and difficult to solve, that I consider the United States to be most fortunate to have one state at least display the liberality which enabled the Buffalo Laboratory to do such good work. The work done at Buffalo is everywhere recognized in Europe as most helpful and personally, I feel that it would be a great reproach to the whole country to interfere in any way with the progress of research of so promising a character.* In a separate letter dated February 15, 1907, Dr. Osler again expressed his concern that the appropriations for the *Cancer Laboratory* might not be continued. The handwritten postscript is most interesting. *P.S. There is no knowing what a day may bring forth should the Buffalo Laboratory find the cause of cancer, it would be the biggest thing ever done in New York State. The New York Central Railroad would be nothing in comparison.*

**2-5.**

National and worldwide
newspaper clippings
tell the progress in
cancer research since
the opening of Gratwick
Research Laboratory.

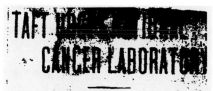

## TAFT ~~HOUSE~~ ~~FOR~~ CANCER LABORATORY

### Asks Congress to Appropriate $50,000 for Study of Disease.

## SUBJECT IS IMPORTANT

1910

WASHINGTON, April 8.—President Taft sent to Congress today a message that may result in important developments in the study of the cause of cancer.

The President asks an appropriation of $50,000 for a laboratory in which to conduct investigations, and transmits the recommendations of the Secretary of Commerce and Labor, the Commissioner of Fisheries, and of Dr. N. E. Gaylord, director of the New York state cancer laboratory, for an inquiry into the cause of cancer in fishes.

"The very great importance of pursuing the investigation into the cause of cancer," said the President, "cannot be brought home to the congress or to the public more acutely than by inviting attention to the memorandum of Dr. Gaylord herewith.

"Progress in the prevention and treatment of human diseases has been marvelously aided by an investigation into the same disease in those of the lower animals which are subject to it, and we have every reason to believe that a close investigation into the subject of cancer in fishes, which are frequently swept away by an epidemic of it, may give us light upon this dreadful human scourge."

## CANCER CURE IN SIGHT

### Few More Years Should Yield Results.

### Notable Conference in Paris Comes to an End.

### Experts Approve Use of Surgeon's Knife, Combined With Biological Treatment.

1910

Special to The Times-Democrat.

New York, Oct. 9.—A cablegram to the Sun from Paris says:

The second Triennial International Conference on the Study of Cancer concluded its five days' meeting last night. Two hundred and fifty delegates represented twenty-two countries. W. B. Coley, chairman of the Huntington Fund for Cancer Research; James Ewing, of Cornell University; Harvey Gaylord, of the New York State laboratory, and S. P. Beebe, of Cornell, were America's representatives.

Dr. Gaylord read a paper on "Passive Immunity in Cancer," describing studies of cancer in fish. Dr. Beebe read a paper of the chemistry of cancer. The chief question discussed was whether cancer is parasitic or nonparasitic. The burden of proof seemed to lie on the upholders of the parasitic theory, as a majority of the delegates do not believe in a specific parasite.

New methods of treatment were exhaustively discussed. Surgery was unanimously approved if it were possible totally to remove the growth. It was generally agreed that radium, X-rays and high, frequent currents were of some value in cases of tumors, upon which operations are not practiced, especially superficial ones, but all three were considered only as palliative treatment, needing combination with biological treatment by serum vaccination.

Every one seemed confident that a few years more study along the latter lines would yield solid results. Three cases of cures by vaccination in Paris were described. The treatment is not painful, and is founded on a scientific basis.

## TELLS OF PROGRESS IN CANCER FIGHT

Hearald, NYC - 4/4/1917

### Dr. Gaylord Warns Public of Neglect of Early Diagnosis—Calls for Army of Nurses.

Speaking under the auspices of the American Society for the Control of Cancer at the Woman's Hospital last night, Dr. Harvey R. Gaylord said "cancer will be with us longer than the war" and that "nurses must take a leading part in the campaign against this malady." Dr. Gaylord is director of the New York State Institute for the Study of Malignant Disease.

Unfortunately, the public too often thinks that cancer is a hopeless, incurable disease, a diagnosis of which is equivalent to a sentence of death," said Dr. Gaylord. "This is not true, and the first step toward reducing the excessive cancer mortality, which now amounts to 80,000 deaths a year in the United States, is to spread the message of hope that this disease can be cured if promptly recognized and treated in the beginning.

"Moreover, there are many different forms of cancer, some of which are more easily cured than others. The importance of having nurses familiar with the facts is that many patients will discuss with nurses signs and symptoms which are beginning to cause apprehension long before they make up their minds to go to a doctor.

"Early diagnosis is the first great essential. We have learned that cancer starts from a small local beginning and that all lesions such as small sores and lumps that do not go away and that are subject to irritation represent cancer possibilities for middle or later life. It is in a weak spot usually that a cancer develops."

**2-6.**
President Taft's and
President Nixon's
signatures in Guest Book.

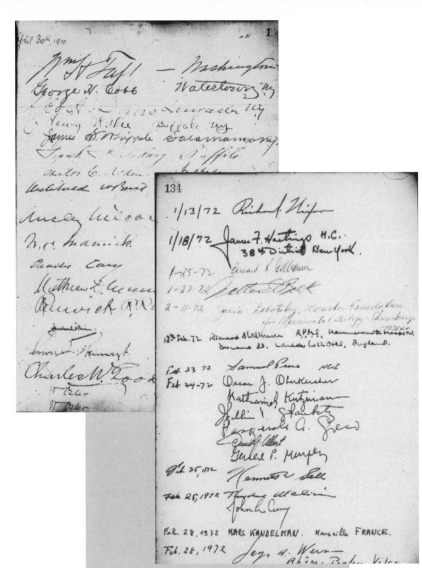

In a report by Dr. Gaylord to the New York State Commissioner of Health February 1, 1908, Dr. Gaylord stated: *During the last five years, the experimental investigation of cancer has broadened to such an extent that many investigators in different parts of the world are now pressing into the field, national institutes and societies have been founded and an international society for the investigation and combatting of cancer is in the process of formation. Today, the outlook in cancer research is not only encouraging but distinctly promising. If one calls to mind the pessimism which reigned 10 years ago regarding cancer, and realizes today how differently the whole disease is viewed, how actively investigators are hopefully working upon the problem and how promising is the outlook, one must concede that the results obtained are far greater than we could have possibly promised ourselves at the time this laboratory was founded by the State.*

Drs. Gaylord and Clowes were influential in the establishment and growth of the American Association for Cancer Research (AACR). Both were charter members who participated in organizational meetings May 7–8, 1907, and hosted in Buffalo the national meeting of the AACR in 1908. While president of the AACR, Dr. Gaylord was authorized to submit a resolution to President William H. Taft proposing the creation of a department of cancer research within a national bureau of health. President Taft visited the Gratwick Research Laboratory in 1910 to enthusiastically support the AACR resolution. The Institute's Guest Book records his visit on April 30, 1910: William H. Taft, Washington, D.C. After leaving the Gratwick Research Laboratory, President Taft turned to Dr. Gaylord and said: *It has been a pleasure for me to visit the laboratory. I hope that the time is not too far distant when we shall have a similar institution under the auspices of the United States.*

The Guest Book of the Roswell Park Cancer Institute contains signatures of many internationally known personages, including Governor Nelson A. Rockefeller, Madame Curie and her daughter, Irene, former Governors Thomas E. Dewey and Alfred E. Smith, and Sir William Osler. Two U.S. presidents have signed the Roswell Park Guest Book: William H. Taft, in 1910, and Richard M. Nixon, in 1972.

After a visit to the Institute, President Taft unsuccessfully appealed to Congress in 1910 for a $50,000 appropriation to create a Department for Cancer Research in the Federal Government. In 1971, however, sixty-one years later, President Nixon signed the National Cancer Act, which called for more than $1,000,000 to promote a National Cancer Program.

**2-7.**
President William H.
Taft. From President
Taft's visit to Roswell
Park in 1910, to Governor
Franklin D. Roosevelt's
visit in 1930, and
Congressman Paul G.
Rogers' National Cancer
Act hearings at Roswell
Park in 1971, Roswell
Park has played a
significant role in getting
the federal government
to support a National
Cancer Program.

# STATE SHOULD AID CANCER RESEARCHES

Dr. Gaylord Tells of
Successful Work in
Asking for Appropria-
tion to Enlarge Use-
fulness of Gratwick
Laboratory.

## BENEFIT TO THE PEOPLE

*1911*

Buffalo Evening News Bureau.
No. 132 State St.

ALBANY, March 16.—Dr. Harvey R.
Gaylord and Assemblyman La Reau
appeared before the Ways and Means
Committee of the Assembly yesterday
afternoon in support of the latter's
bill appropriating $65,000 for the erec-
tion of a hospital building and the
establishing of a State institute for
study of malignant diseases on condition that the present Gratwick
laboratory property in Buffalo shall
be presented to the State by Mrs
William H. Gratwick.

"The people of Buffalo," said Mr
LeReau, "are much interested in the
work of the institution and helped sup
port it both before and after the State
made provision for the study of cancer. The money is wisely expended
and I think it is generally recognized
that the laboratory is the original in
stitution of its kind in the world.

### Studied by Scientists.

"Scientists from Germany and other
parts of the world have come to Buffalo to study its methods and gone
back home to establish similar institutions. The State Health Commissioner has heartily indorsed its work,
and it remains only for the State to
make it a permanent benefit to the
people, not only of New York State,
but of the whole world."

Dr. Gaylord outlined briefly the
work that has been done in experimenting, giving credit in this connection to Dr. Roswell Park, whom he
named as one of the world's greatest
surgeons.

"Dr. Park," said Dr. Gaylord, "decided that the investigation of cancer
was not going beyond the academic
phase and he first started the present
research and investigation of what to
the medical fraternity is today the
modern sphinx—cancer. He it was
who conceived the idea that cancer
had not been treated as a problem by
itself."

# TAFT ASKS CANCER CRUSADE BY U.S.

*1910*

WASHINGTON. April 9.—Recommending an appropriation of fifty
thousand dollars for laboratories to
deal with the problem of cancers as
transmitted by fishes, President Taft
today sent to Congress a special message embracing reports from the Secretary of Commerce and Labor, the
Commissioner of Fisheries and Dr. H.
L. Gaylord, director of the New York
State Cancer Laboratories.

The President suggests immediate
action should be taken to provide for
an investigation as to the prevalence
of cancer in fish and the possibility of
its being transferred to human beings
through using the fish for food.

**2-8.**
Newspaper clippings
on April 9, 1910,
indicating President
Taft's support of
a National Cancer
Crusade and National
Cancer Laboratory.

# TAFT URGES NATIONAL CANCER LABORATORY

Asks Congress to Appropriate
$50,000 for Study of
Disease.

## SUBJECT IS IMPORTANT

WASHINGTON, April 9.—
President Taft sent to Congress today
a message that may result in important
developments in the study of the causes
of cancer.

The President asks an appropriation
of $50,000 for a laboratory in which to
conduct investigations, and transmits the
recommendations of the Secretary of
Commerce and Labor, the Commissioner
of Fisheries, and of Dr. N. E. Gaylord,
director of the New York state cancer
laboratory, for an inquiry into the cause
of cancer in fishes.

"The very great importance of pursuing
the investigation into the cause of cancer," said the President, "cannot be
brought home to the congress or to the
public more acutely than by inviting attention to the memorandum of Dr. Gaylord herewith.

"Progress in the prevention and treatment of human diseases has been marvelously aided by an investigation into
the same disease in those of the lower
animals which are subject to it, and we
have every reason to believe that a close
investigation into the subject of cancer
in fishes, which are frequently swept
away by an epidemic of it, may give us
light upon this dreadful human scourge."

President Taft had shown great interest in the work being done at the Institute in conjunction with the U.S. Bureau of Fisheries of the Department of Commerce and Labor with Commissioner G. M. Bowers. He had included the recommendations of Drs. Park and Gaylord in his message to Congress April 9, 1910, stating that the federal government should support cancer programs and particularly support an appropriation of $50,000 to the Institute to erect one or more laboratories. President Taft stated, *The very great importance of pursuing the investigation into the cause of cancer cannot be brought home to the Congress or the public more acutely,* and in his message he cites the contributions of Dr. Gaylord. He continued by saying, *Close investigation into the subject of cancer may give us light upon this dreadful human scourge.* The bill presented to the Sixty-first Congress passed the Senate but failed in the House of Representatives. Although President Taft supported a federal cancer program, this was not realized until, first, President Franklin D. Roosevelt (who as Governor of New York was familiar with Roswell Park and its cancer programs) and, then, President Richard M. Nixon made research on the problem of cancer a national goal through passage of the National Cancer Act in 1937 and the National Cancer Act in 1971, respectively.

Around this time, Dr. Roswell Park and Dr. Harvey Gaylord realized that a hospital was needed where laboratory findings could be given clinical application and further clinical investigation could be done on radium and x-ray treatments. *The time has come when the State Cancer Laboratory should have hospital facilities for research purposes. All the great modern institutions of medical research are so equipped.—Dr. Gaylord, 1911.*

The Gratwick Research Laboratory was maintained through an annual grant from New York State, but the State owned neither the facility nor the land on which it was built. The University of Buffalo acquired both the land and the building on October 10, 1900. Dr. Park, realizing *an ever-varying legislature and the necessity of an annual struggle for existence,* urged Dr. Gaylord to have the laboratory completely owned by New York State. In 1911, Dr. Park, with the help of Senators Hill, Loomis, and Burd, Assemblyman LaReau, and with the continuous help and encouragement of John Lord O'Brian, Ansley Wilcox, Dean Alden of the Law Department of the University of Buffalo, and other interested citizens, succeeded in making the Gratwick Research Laboratory a State Institute. Their accomplishment is recorded in Laws of the State of New York, Chapter 128, May 10, 1911.

The University of Buffalo provided affidavits from Chancellor Charles P. Norton and Secretary of the University Frank M. Hollister, and a resolution passed by fourteen of twenty members of the UB Council on February 22, 1912, to transfer the Gratwick Research Laboratory and property on February 29, 1912, to the people of New York State. From this transfer, for which UB received no compensation, the Gratwick Research Laboratory became the New York State Institute for the Study of Malignant Diseases.

*The citizens of Buffalo are prepared to deed to the State $95,000 worth of property, including the handsome laboratory erected by Mrs. William H. Gratwick, thus tendering to the State a complete institution with a site for the necessary hospital,* stated Dr. Gaylord, in 1911. The Gratwick Research Laboratory was officially transferred to New York State February 29, 1912, after legislation, Chapter 128, May 10, 1911, allowed New York State to accept the properties. The parcel of land at High and Oak Streets was deeded to the State March 7, 1912, as recorded in Liber 1239 of Deeds at page 309. State Senate Bill 75 further provided for a Board of Trustees and for the organization of the Institute.

Research during this period still included study of
the preparation and action of vaccines, the search
for parasites as a possible cause of cancer, transplantation studies of mouse and fish tumors, and
investigations of immune reactions. The need to
apply findings to clinical treatment in human subjects became evident. Therefore, the Cary Pavilion
was built for this purpose on the property at High
and Oak Streets.

The Cary Pavilion was the first hospital building
to be constructed at the Institute. This elegant
thirty-bed facility was named for Dr. Charles
Cary, one of the first and most involved and dedicated trustees of the Institute. Dr. Cary made
daily visits to keep in touch with the operation of
the facility from 1898 until his death in 1931. Dr.
Cary's name is still part of the Institute, with a
meeting room in the Research Studies Center
named in his honor.

The Cary Pavilion was designed by Dr. Cary's
brother, George, a prominent local architect.
A number of citizens contributed toward the pur-
chase of the property on which the Cary Pavilion
was erected, and donated it to the State of New
York, including: Martha Gratwick; Frank B. Baird;
Frank L. Babst; Sarah Becker; George K. Birge;
George Bleistein; S. M. Clement; Charles Clifton;
William H. Crosby; Mrs. Charles Daniels; O. E.
Foster; Robert L. Fryer; Mrs. C. W. Goodyear;
Josephine Goodyear; A. C. Goodyear; W. H.
Gratwick; F. C. Gratwick; Chauncey J. Hamlin;
Mrs. Harry Hamlin; Edmund Hayes; William H.
Hotchkiss; George R. Howard; William B. Hoyt;
Charles R. Huntley; Dudley M. Irwin; Spencer
Kellogg; Kenefick, Cooke, Mitchell & Bass; S. H.
Knox; J. D. Larkin; Franklin D. Locke; George B.
Mathews; John G. Milburn; Adelbert Moot; C. W.
Pardee; George F. Rand; Sarah Cook Reeder;
Henry Richmond; William A. Rodgers; Robert K.
Root; Susan Fiske Rumsey; L. D. Rumsey; Hans
Schmidt; Mrs. Albert Schoellkopf; C. P. Hugo
Schoellkopf; Carlton Smith; Henry W. Sprague;
Frederick H. Stevens; Hattie Brooks Stevens;
George Urban, Jr.; Genevieve von Berge; Grace
Rumsey Wilcox; and Henry Yates.

**2-10.**
The Cary Pavilion
was our first elegant
thirty-bed hospital
(dedicated on November
1, 1913). Dr. James
Ewing, internationally
known professor of
Pathology and later
long-term trustee,
was the main speaker
at the dedication.

# Local Hospital for Study of Malignant Diseases is Opened

## Dr. Roswell Park Who Presided at Formal Opening Praises Edward H. Butler for His Co-operation in Establishing Laboratory.

Formal opening yesterday of the hospital in connection with the State Institute for the Study of Malignant Disease was celebrated by the trustees of the Institute and 150 Buffalo physicians and friends of the cancer laboratory with simple but interesting exercises.

The addresses were delivered in Alumni hall at the University of Buffalo in High street. Dr. Roswell Park, chairman of the trustees of the institute presiding and delivering one of the addresses.

The new hospital in High street was thrown open yesterday afternoon for inspection and was visited by a large number of those who are interested in the study of cancer, which is being conducted in the institute by Dr. Harvey R. Gaylord, its director, and many who have been supporters of the Gratwick laboratory. The handsome building and its hospital equipment were highly praised by all who inspected the place, especially the physicians.

### Notables Attend Opening.

Dr. ........... origin and the hand ... continuous work done for 15 or 20 years to awaken realization of the necessity for the study of cancer disease and to procure the co-operation of citizens and the state, with the result that the Buffalo cancer laboratory and hospital are now accomplished factors in the effort of medical science to fathom the cause and to find the preventative or cure of cancer.

### Praise for Workers.

Chairman Park praised those who had been instrumental in procuring the co-operation of state authorities and legislation which enabled the establishing of the laboratory and the hospital, including Edward H. Butler, Henry W. Hill, former state senator, former senators Frank M. Loomis, Oliver G. LaRue, former Senator George B. Hurd, these men, with others, said Dr. Park, realized the value to the state of investigation of the causes of cancer with the purpose of determining the cure, and their work contributed greatly to the action by the state which resulted yesterday in the formal opening of the hospital.

"When I removed here from the West, some 30 years ago," said Dr. Park, "I was impressed with the relative frequency with which cancer and allied disorders were found in Western New York, as compared with the region which I had left. I was impressed also with the meagerness of our knowledge concerning the disease and of just appreciation of its import, its clinical characteristics, and its dangers to the community at large."

### Black Vetoed Bill.

Then began the study of the nature of cancer and its prevalence, this investigation ultimately leading to the state for financial aid. Warm friends of the measure, said Chairman Park, were found in former Governor Frank W. Higgins and Hon. S. Fred Nixon, who then was chairman of the Assembly Ways and Means committee. Through their efforts a bill was passed in the Legislature in 1897, which was vetoed by Governor Black.

"The following year," continued Dr. Park, "the measure was again introduced and passed. At this time Mr. Edward H. Butler of this city lent his personal and powerful aid toward securing from Governor Black such change of views as induced him to sign the appropriation. In this way, and in the year 1898, was secured from the New York State Legislature the first appropriation ever made for this purpose from public funds, either in this country or abroad. This money was appropriated to the medical department of the University of Buffalo, for purpose of inaugurating and financing its first stage."

In connection with the institution for investigation of the dread disease, Dr. Park cited the numerous advantages possessed by the local institute, as a part of the state's machinery for the study of disease. He sketched the history of cancer, touched on the X-Ray and radium as possible, but as yet undetermined factors in the discovery of cause and in the cure of cancer. In conclusion Dr. Park urged support of the state institute and, incidentally, referring to the X-Ray and radium, he said:

### Great Interest Aroused.

"So great has been the interest recently aroused in these two elements that municipalities and wealthy philanthropists have devoted large sums of money to their securement and their trial in this disease. Various cities in Europe have voted large sums of money and various organizations have been offered for the purchase and suitable use of radium preparations in selected institutions and upon selected patients.

"Thus we hear of various 'radium institutes' and the like, most of them being ........ An appeal will be m....... for money to m........ will to ........................ this direction can ........ may be made to private benevolence. No matter how it may be secured, those who provide it can be assured of its proper and legitimate use.

"Were it possible to protect the thousands of ignorant and innocent victims of cancer in this state so that the money which they spend on the so-called 'cancer cures' and institutions advertised for this purpose, no words expended in the effort could be too forcible nor too greatly to the point. So long as the public enjoy support imposters, so long will the day be delayed when one genuinely interested in the race can feel that for the poor cancer patient everything is being done that science or philanthropy can offer."

### Cancer Research a Necessity.

Mr. Fairchild spoke enthusiastically of the Buffalo institute and its importance as the leader in the investigation of cancer in this country. He compared the necessity and importance of cancer research in this state with the barge canal, the good roads, and similar works for which the state is expending millions as against the few thousands that it is giving to the cancer investigation. He urged the necessity for state and individual support of the institution that its researches may be thorough and that they may prove of benefit to medical science and to mankind.

"The state should be a supporter of this work," said Mr. Fairchild in conclusion. "If this work fulfills its bright promises the state will find that the little sums of money it has given toward this institution will redound to the credit of New York state, when its barge canal and good roads will have been forgotten. It is a great honor to the state, to Buffalo and to individuals to be connected with this great and vital work, to have even the least part in promoting and progressing it."

### Prof. Ewing Discusses Cancer.

The third address was delivered by Professor James Ewing of Cornell University Medical school who spoke on "Research Hospital." Professor Ewing gave a brief history of the discoveries made in the study of cancer; recited the difficulties which stand in the way of discovery from superficial study ........................ ......... ............... ........... afforded by the Buffalo hospital.

In the hospital, said the physician, the patients will be studied, the symptoms of cancer may be closely and accurately learned, more correct diagnosis may be made and therefore, greater progress may be expected toward ascertaining the causes of cancer and determining what best will serve as a preventative or cure.

Dr. Ewing also stated the many theories as to cancer and the few discoveries which are rated as substantial, and he emphasized the value of the Buffalo hospital as a means of facilitating resultful research and also the necessity that philanthropists as well as the state must support the institution, that it may have every facility with which to prosecute its great work in behalf of humanity and the science of medicine.

2-12.

Excerpt from article
in NEW YORK TIMES
describing details
of the Cary Pavilion.

The hospital is semi-circular. The entire effect is quite original and very pleasing from an architectural point of view. Mr. George Cary of Buffalo, architect of the Buffalo General hospital, also designed these buildings.

In the hospital are two wards accommodating seven patients each. There are also about a dozen private rooms for the segregation of especially malignant or contagious cases. It is a noiseless hospital. The beds are rolled about on rubber wheels that make no sound. There are no bells. A patient desiring attendance merely presses a button that illuminates a number of electric bulbs throughout the building, calling the attention of the attendant, no matter where the latter may be. Even the light is not permitted to shine in the patients' eyes in this hospital. The illumination is thrown upward to the ceiling, whence it is reflected downward, whereby an even, non-brilliant light is diffused through the wards. The elevators are electrically automatic, moving noiselessly to the desired floors merely by the pressing of a button. No elevator attendant is required.

Even the bathtubs are extraordinary. Thirty seconds after the water has been turned on the tubs are sufficiently filled for the purpose. The solaria, or sun parlors, can be metamorphosed into sleeping porches simply by opening the windows and introducing the beds. The latter are furnished with electric pads for the purpose of maintaining sufficient warmth for the patients, who at the same time are enjoying the benefit of the open air.

Every conceivable appliance for the minimizing of effort and sound and for the elimination of unsanitary conditions is in use in this most modern of hospitals. It is perhaps the most electric and at the same time automatic institution in the city of Buffalo and perhaps in the state of New York. The coves are run flush with the walls, so that no dust can accumulate thereon. There are very few ledges of any description. The doors are unpanelled. There are no mantels. The radiators are covered with white metal covers which regulate

or otherwise without having been in contact with anybody or substance.

The refrigeration system is one of the most complete in the world. The dumb waiters are electric and automatic. The X-ray room with its wonderful contrivances is a maze of mystery in the midst of which the intricate details of the progress of internal disease can be minutely observed and studied. The kitchen harbors the most modern of culinary appliances. The last word in the use of preparation

of inspection a portable telephone. As he notes the symptoms of each patient he will speak into this portable telephone, which will communicate his voice to a loud-talking box telephone in his private office. His stenographer, sitting at her typewriter, will immediately write the descriptions of the symptoms, etc., as they fall from the surgeon's lips. Thus, upon his return to his office, he will have before him an accurate typewritten record of everything that he has noted during

2-13.

Private room in
the Cary Pavilion.

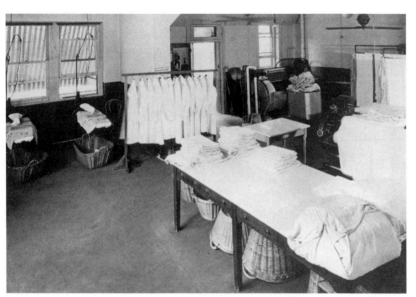

**2-14.**
Laundry room in the
Cary Pavilion.

The land was valued at $21,000 and New York State appropriated $140,000 for construction of the hospital. Dedication ceremonies were held for the Cary Pavilion November 1, 1913, in Alumni Hall at the University of Buffalo School of Medicine, then located on High Street. Speakers included Dr. Roswell Park, the Honorable Charles S. Fairchild (trustee and former secretary of the treasury in President Cleveland's administration), and the principal speaker, Dr. James Ewing, internationally renowned professor of Pathology at the Cornell University Medical School. Dr. Ewing, who was well aware of Dr. Park's philosophy for a cancer center, actively engaged in research through his interactions with our staff and as our trustee for many years. He, too, was convinced that the progress of cancer research was inextricably bound to the development of a cancer research hospital where research could be directly applied to the treatment of human cancer. This had much to do with his plans and reorganization of Memorial Hospital in New York City during his tenure as director of that facility from 1913 to 1939.

In his remarks November 1, Dr. Ewing said: *It is a growing conviction that to know cancer in man, one must study the disease most carefully in the human subject. Personally, I do not look for any startling advances or sensational discoveries, since it is more likely that a steady reduction in the mortality from cancer will come chiefly from a large number of separate factors, of which the most significant appear to be, increased control of the conditions leading to cancer, more general recognition of the preliminary stages of the disease, early diagnosis and treatment of the established disease. From the consideration of these various functions of the modern cancer research hospital, I think that it must be evident that such an institution not only can justify its existence, but fills a very urgent need without which, progress of cancer research would be handicapped; much relief that might early be extended to cancer victims would be unavailable. Nor, is there any doubt that the function of supporting such an institution is properly exercised by the State, which support should be continuous and liberal.*

Five registered nurses were on staff at Cary Pavilion, under the supervision of Mrs. Katherine H. Danner, superintendent of the Department of Nursing, to care for patients.

Another very significant event in 1913 was the establishment of Statewide Pathological Services at the Institute, with Dr. Burton T. Simpson as chief pathologist. Physicians and dentists statewide could now send specimens to the Institute for microscopic examination for the diagnosis of cancer at no cost. To date, pathological diagnosis of cancer had not been well integrated into hospital and university settings. This model had a great impact on cancer diagnosis and resulted in its adoption in other states.

2-15.
Early mouse laboratory
at the Biological Station
at Springville.

While the Cary Pavilion marked the beginning of the clinical program, the research program also was expanding in 1913. Ten local citizens (Thomas F. Cooke, William H. Gratwick, Charles Cary, Harry Yates, F. C. Gratwick, Roswell Park, Frank B. Baird, Robert Pomeroy, Harvey R. Gaylord, and Dudley Irwin) purchased an experimental farm near Springville, New York, a village about thirty miles south of Buffalo. The property, an area of thirty-one acres (now nineteen acres) containing nineteen springs, was chosen by Drs. Cary and Gaylord with the help of a local physician, Dr. Mark N. Brooks. After legislative action made it possible for the Institute to receive gifts and bequests, the Springville property was presented to Dr. Gaylord by several Institute trustees and physicians from Buffalo. Dr. Roswell Park, the Honorable Charles S. Fairchild, Dr. Charles Cary, and Frederick H. Stevens were the trustees at this time.

New York State provided $15,000 and $21,000 for development of the farm. Mr. Millard C. Marsh was appointed first director of the Biological Station at Springville. Mr. Marsh collaborated with Dr. Gaylord in the study of thyroid tumors in trout, and began mouse breeding experiments to determine the relation between susceptibility to malignant disease and hereditary. In 1915, the trustees recommended further expansion of the Biological Station, and requested a State grant of $20,000. The Biological Station was expanded again in 1932 when a laboratory building was constructed.

Dr. Roswell Park died February 15, 1914, at the age of sixty-one after a short attack of syncope, as he would have wished, quietly. The Honorable Charles S. Fairchild succeeded him as chairman of the Board on March 12, 1914. The Board of Trustees passed the following resolution which had been proposed by Dr. Cary, and sent it to the Park family: *The original inception of an institute supported by the State for the investigation of cancer was Dr. Park's. Through his friends in the Legislature he secured the first appropriation for the laboratory, now the Institute. Although the first appropriation was vetoed by Governor Black, he persisted and in 1898 again secured the passage of an appropriation of ten thousand dollars, which received the approval of the Governor. In its formative state he was director of the laboratory but shortly withdrew therefrom and acted in an advisory capacity in the work, and in 1911, on the passage of the bill creating the Institute, he became chairman of the first board of trustees. The board of trustees recognizes the vision and farsightedness of his original inception and feels in his passing an irreparable loss to the interests of the work. It is a matter of great satisfaction that he saw before his death the realization of an enlarged and comprehensive Institute, which will remain for all time a monument to his initiative.*

**2-17.**
Painting of Dr. Roswell
Park and Dr. Roswell
Park Medal given by
Roswell Park Surgical
Society.

**2-18.**
Death masque of
Dr. Roswell Park and
excerpt from Roswell
Park obituary in
BUFFALO COURIER
EXPRESS February
18, 1914.

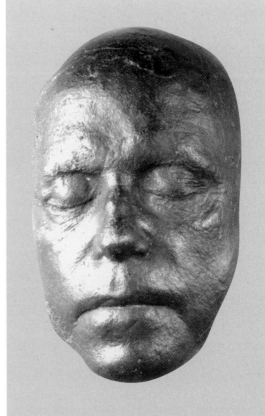

"Two death masques of Dr. Park were taken by
Dr. Charles W. Bethune just previous to the
cremation. One was a profile view and the other
a full face impression. The skin was oiled, the
hair vaselined, and French dental plaster poured
over the features. Both masques are said to
be perfect likenesses.

"An attempt was made to take an impression of
the right hand but it did not prove successful due
to the natural contraction of that member. Had
it resulted satisfactorily casts of the famous surgeon's hand would have been presented to the
larger organizations of which he was a member.

"It was stated last night a bronze bust of Dr. Park
will be presented by the Academy of Medicine
to the University of Buffalo. For the present,
however, the two precious masques are in the
joint custody of Dr. Bethune, the Academy of
Medicine and the University."

**2-19.**

Dr. and Mrs. Byron Koekkoek in front of Dr. Roswell Park's painting. Mrs. Koekkoek is the granddaughter of Dr. Roswell Park. Left to right: Dr. Koekkoek, Mrs. Koekkoek, and Dr. E. A. Mirand.

Dr. Park had been referred to as a Renaissance man: . . . *vigorous, handsome, highly trained; possessed with the traditions of learning, a pervading sense of humor and air of distinction. A man of boundless energy who quickly formed an extensive acquaintance among the foremost wherever he went.* He was plagued by ill health with tracheal stenosis in the last year of his life. However, following a heart attack, he returned to the hospital and teaching with his customary verve and skill. He was also prophetic. The morning after his death, Dr. A. L. Benedict, editor and publisher of the BUFFALO MEDICAL JOURNAL, received a letter from Dr. Park, his last one, delegating certain duties on a committee and containing these words: *Within two or three days I hope to be able to get away for a much needed rest of somewhat indefinite length.* Dr. Park's pride in the progress made at the Institute was evident in his statement in the NEW YORK STATE JOURNAL OF MEDICINE, Volume 7, Number 5, page 189, 1907: *There can be no doubt that if any unprejudiced person will visit the institution and acquaint himself with what is doing and has been done he will leave it feeling that it is one of which New York State may well be proud, and that it is deserving of the heartiest public support.*

In 1914, through the urging of Trustee Dr. James Ewing, the Institute became one of the earliest centers to use radium in the treatment of cancer. With a generous donation of $6,000 from Mrs. Ansley Wilcox, the Institute purchased its first radium (50 milligrams) and used it to treat cancers of the cervix, tongue, prostate, and skin. A few years later, New York State's Gibbs Bill appropriated $225,000 for the purchase of two and one-half grams of radium from Radiochemical Corporation of New York, which mined carnotite ore in Colorado and extracted radium in Orange, New Jersey. On July 20, 1920, Governor Alfred E. Smith made an elaborate release on this purchase, saying: *The radium will be used scientifically for research and treatment purposes by Dr. Gaylord and his staff, and with this amount of radium at its disposal, New York will be in the forefront of states working for the treatment of cancer and other malignant growths.* The NEW YORK TIMES commented on the purchase of radium on August 2, 1920, stating that *the New York Institution now leads the country in the fight against cancer and will begin next fall to furnish free radium treatments to sufferers of this disease who request it.*

# FIRST GIFT OF RADIUM, TO GRATWICK LABORATORY, IS BY MRS. ANSLEY WILCOX

## Fifty Milligrams of Almost Priceless Extract of Ore to Be Delivered in April at Cost of $6,000 — Trustees Hope Other Public-spirited Residents Will Be as Generous as Woman Has Been.

### ONLY ONE-FIFTH OF AMOUNT SO URGENTLY NEEDED IS IN BUFFALO

The constant stream of favorable reports showing radium is to play an important role in the cure of cancer, the demonstrated certainty that it already cures superficial cancer, and the remarkable results obtained with large growths of the sarcoma type (connective tissue cancer), as well as the fact that certain inoperable cases of cancer among women have been cured by radium, have so stimulated interest in Buffalo that the present position of the Gratwick laboratory, which although one of the first centers of research in the world, has not yet had at its disposal for study and experimental treatment any radium, is regrettable.

It is with great pleasure, therefore, that the laboratory is today able to announce that it has received a gift of fifty milligrams of radium. The public spirited donor is Mrs. Ansley Wilcox who has come forward and authorized Dr. Charles Cary of the board of trustees of the laboratory to place an order with the Radium Chemical company of Pittsburgh for fifty milligrams of radium to be delivered in April. The purchase price of this amount of radium is $6,000.

**First Working Amount.**

Although there have been small amounts of radium in Buffalo, this fifty milligrams will be the first working amount of radium in the city, and it will be the first step toward supplying the laboratory with a sufficient amount to enable it to treat successfully the more difficult cases. Mrs. Wilcox's public spirit and generosity will place in the hands of the laboratory enough radium for experimental purposes and enable the scientific workers of the laboratory to acquire a knowledge of radium and of its action. An attempt will be made during the present session of the legislature to have the state appropriate an additional sum. It is hoped, now that Mrs. Wilcox has made this first generous contribution to secure the first unit for effective radium treatment, that possibly other public-spirited citizens who are vitally interested in the securing for Buffalo of a sufficient amount of radium, will come forward. The quantity of radium in Buffalo is only one-fifth of this amount needed to meet present demands.

**Supply All Spoken For.**

The demand for radium is increasing so rapidly that the supplies for this country have already been taken up until August, and although there is some prospect that the production of radium will increase, it is hoped the legislature will act promptly, that through its agency and possibly by other private benefaction, a sufficient amount may be secured for delivery within the coming year.

In 1930, at the request of Governor Franklin D. Roosevelt, the legislature appropriated $300,000 for the purchase of an additional 5,737 milligrams of radium, necessary containers and other apparatus for its operation and storage. This purchase increased the amount of radium at the Institute to 7,774 milligrams, the largest amount available at any one place for treatment of cancer and experimental purposes. Governor Roosevelt was very familiar with the cancer program at the Institute. When he visited Roswell Park in 1930, he urged the Institute to develop satellite cancer units across the State for cancer treatment. As President, this familiarity with Roswell Park led him to support and sign the National Cancer Act of 1937 which formulated the National Cancer Institute. In a conversation with Dr. Edwin A. Mirand on October 27, 1955, on her visit to Buffalo, Mrs. Eleanor Roosevelt recalled the visit that then Governor Franklin Roosevelt made to the Institute in 1930, and that his familiarity with the cancer programs at the Institute and New York State had strongly influenced his future actions to support national cancer programs as President, particularly the National Cancer Act of 1937.

In 1917 Dr. Gaylord was given military leave, and Dr. Burton T. Simpson was named acting director. During 1917 and 1918, Mr. Marsh continued his studies at the Biological Station at Springville on the incidence of cancer in inbred mice and the effects of trauma in relation to cancer.

Dr. Gaylord still believed in the parasitic theory of the origin of cancer. In 1919 he requested Dr. Peyton Rous, who was very familiar with the early work of the Institute in this area, to send to the Institute a Plymouth Rock fowl bearing a tumor induced by a virus. For several years, the staff worked with this viral tumor. It is indicative of Dr. Gaylord's farsightedness that he recognized the importance of the work that Dr. Rous had performed in 1911; it was not until 1966 that Dr. Rous received a Nobel Prize for that same work.

In 1921 the first 200,000-volt x-ray machine was installed at the Institute, making it possible to compare cancer treatment using radium with that using x-rays. The following year, important advances were made in the clinical use of x-ray and radium therapy by the Institute. This work was recognized internationally when Madame Marie Curie, from the University of Paris, discoverer of radium and twice awarded the Nobel Prize, and her daughter, Irene, visited the Institute June 17, 1921. The page of the Guest Book for June 17, 1921, is headed by the entry, *M. Curie, University of Paris, and her daughter, I. Curie.* While in Buffalo, they stayed for several weeks with Roswell Park staff members, Dr. Hollis Hunt DiNord and Dr. Richard DiNord at 182 Franklin Street. Madame Curie lectured on the effects of radiation on thyroid tumors. She had conversations with Dr. Burton Simpson and staff physicist Dr. K. Wilhelm Stenstrom on radium and x-ray studies at the Institute. Mrs. Gaylord, in the absence of Dr. Gaylord, who was with Professor Aschoff in Freiburg, Germany, had made arrangements for her social entertainment. Prior to her arrival in Buffalo, Madame Curie had a strenuous time in Philadelphia and New York City at Memorial Hospital. Because of the arduous schedule, the excitement, and her physical weakness, some of her itinerary had been curtailed.

In 1974 the Institute established the annual Madame Curie Lecture Series to commemorate this visit and her collaboration with Dr. Gaylord. Dr. Walter T. Murphy, a nationally-known radiotherapist and chief of Radiation Therapy at Roswell Park for twenty-four years until his retirement in 1963, presented the first lecture.

Madame Marie Curie and her daughter, Irene, visited the Institute in June 1921. Staff exchanged scientific findings with her, particularly the impact of radium on tumors. While in Buffalo, she visited her childhood friend, Dr. Francis Fronczak, well known and respected Commissioner of Health of Erie County. She stayed with our staff member, Dr. Hollis DiNord for several weeks at 182 Franklin Street. The Madame Curie Lecture memorialized her visit to the Institute and scientific collaboration with the staff at that time. Madame Curie stressed during her visit to the Institute that special attention be paid to the improvement of radiation measurement methods stating "the results of radiation treatment depend on the precise knowledge of the amount of radium applied."

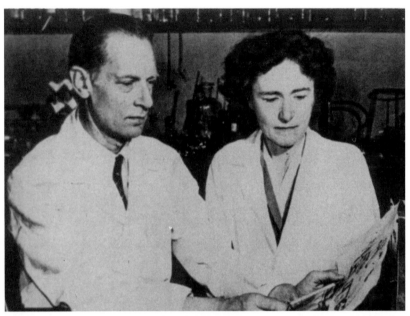

**2-22.**
Dr. Carl Cori and Dr. Gerty Cori in laboratory at Roswell Park.

During travels in Europe, Dr. Gaylord met Drs. Carl and Gerty Cori, and persuaded them to leave Vienna to join the Institute staff. Dr. Gaylord wrote in a letter from Vienna on June 1, 1921: *I have found one young man who seems very promising indeed. His wife is also a doctor and has done laboratory work and could take an assistant position in the laboratory so they could work very well. He speaks some English.* Dr. Carl Cori became head of the Biological Chemistry Department, and Dr. Gerty Cori was appointed assistant pathologist. They left the Institute years later to join the staff of Washington University in St. Louis. Subsequently, they were awarded a Nobel Prize for work which had its genesis at the Institute. Dr. Carl Cori visited Buffalo November 20, 1968, to deliver the first lecture in the Institute's annual Cori Lecture Series, named for him and the late Dr. Gerty Cori. Dr. Cori's topic was ENZYMATIC & MOLECULAR PROPERTIES OF PHOSPHORYLASE. (Dr. Gerty Cori was the first American woman and only the third woman in the world to receive the Nobel Prize.)

The Institute continued to make important advances in the clinical use of x-rays and radium therapy. In 1922 radium treatments reached a high of 843 while 517 deep x-ray treatments were administered. Mrs. L. M. Weinland was appointed superintendent of Nursing in 1923.

In 1923, Dr. Gaylord was given a leave of absence due to ill health. Dr. Burton T. Simpson served as acting Institute director. Dr. Gaylord retired as director April 7, 1924. On April 16, 1924, the Board of Trustees, which included Dr. James Ewing, who had promoted his appointment, named Dr. Simpson Institute director. Dr. Gaylord died at Watkins Glen, New York, on June 21, 1924, at the age of fifty-one. Dr. Gaylord had devoted twenty-five years to the study of cancer. During his nineteen years as Institute Director, he had presided over unprecedented physical and program expansion. Research was innovative, a hospital was constructed, and physicians were trained. He had cast the mold for all of the comprehensive cancer centers that followed based on the philosophy of Dr. Roswell Park. Through his involvement in the formation of the American Association for Cancer Research and contributions to the International Cancer Congress in 1911, he had helped elevate the study of cancer to a worldwide priority, marshaled the greatest scientific minds to the cause, and forged a forceful and significant leadership role for the Institute.

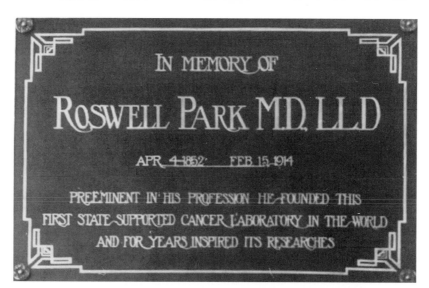

**3-1.**
Dr. Burton T. Simpson in his office in the Gratwick Research Laboratory. He established highly needed and popular statewide pathological diagnostic service in 1913 that continued through his administration. This activity resulted in many referrals to the Institute.

1924

1943

**3-2.**
Dr. Bernard F. Schreiner
was the senior physician
during the Gaylord and
Simpson administrations.
He was a highly respected
physician worshiped by
staff and patients.

Dr. Burton T. Simpson graduated cum laude from
the University of Buffalo Medical School in
1903. From 1904 until 1910 Dr. Simpson taught
embryology and anatomy of the nervous system
at the University of Buffalo. He joined the staff in
1912 as a pathologist in the Gratwick Research
Laboratory and became the third Institute director
in 1924. From 1920, Dr. Simpson had served as
acting director, not continuously, but nearly so,
and became thoroughly familiar with the work of
the office of the director. His administration
included William G. Illinger, Institute steward.
During the Simpson administration, which continued through 1943, more and more emphasis
was placed on clinical activities. Dr. Simpson
noted in an annual report, *While we endeavor to
keep some research study under way in the laboratory, the increase in our routine duties has been
making it more and more difficult to find sufficient
time to devote to these problems.*

A notable staff member during Dr. Simpson's
administration was Dr. Bernard F. Schreiner, a
brilliant surgeon and principal cancer physician,
and one of Dr. Roswell Park's outstanding assistants. To most patients, Dr. Schreiner symbolized
the Institute. Dr. Schreiner was a great advocate
of the nursing staff. He made what appears to be
the first published statement recognizing nurses
in 1927: *The cooperation between clinical and
pathological as well as physical and radiological
laboratories, together with the excellent cooperation on the part of the Nursing staff have contributed largely to the success of our work.*

**3-3.**
The outstanding staff of the Institute in Dr. Simpson's administration received national and international recognition for their deeds; i.e., the Coris received Nobel Prize; Mr. M. Marsh contributed to developing mouse cancer strain distributed worldwide; Dr. Schreiner, Dr. Park's assistant, to most patients symbolized the Institute; Dr. Thibaudeau and Dr. Simpson, noteworthy pathologists; Dr. Mattick and Dr. Stenstrom were well-known contributors to their respective fields.

**3-6.**
Gaylord Building occupied in 1927.

**3-4.**
Dr. Bernard F. Schreiner with senior physicians during Dr. Simpson's administration.

**3-5.**
Senior physicians in Dr. Simpson's administration. Back row, second from left is Dr. Louis Kress, Institute director, 1945–1952.

**3-7.**
Chemistry lab in Gaylord
Building used by
Drs. Carl and Gerty Cori.

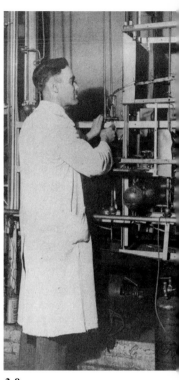

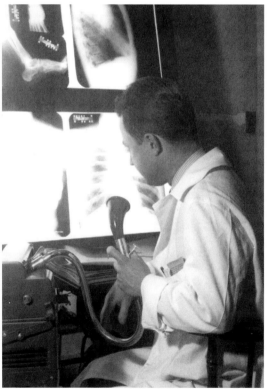

**3-9.**
Technician working in
laboratory in Gaylord
Building.

**3-8.**
Dr. Walter Murphy
reading diagnostic x-rays
in Gaylord Building.

**3-10.**
Mr. Melvin Reinhard, physicist, preparing radium for clinical treatment of patients.

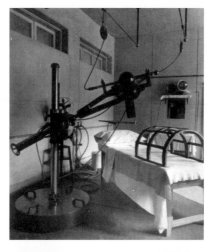

**3-12.**
X-ray machine in the Gaylord Building.

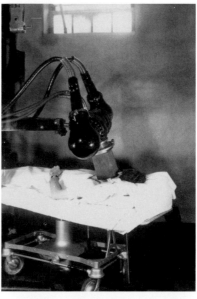

**3-13.**
Patient being treated by early x-ray machine in Gaylord Building.

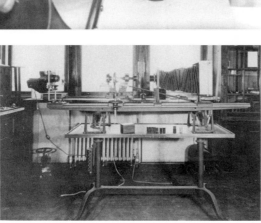

**3-11.**
Photographic room in Gaylord Building used by Mr. William Payne, who trained Dr. Mirand, then a student, to use the equipment in the early 1940s.

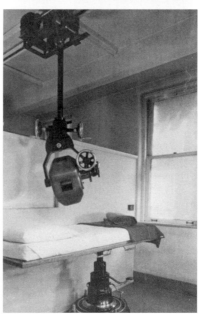

**3-14.**
Diagnostic x-ray room in Gaylord Building.

Governor Alfred E. Smith made the provision of a new hospital building at the Institute part of his early campaign in 1924. This new facility was needed because the number of patients being referred to the Institute by physicians had increased tremendously. Due to this increased demand for services, the Institute required an Outpatient Department, an X-Ray Therapy Department, a Diagnostic X-Ray Department, a Urology Department, and a Record Room. The cost of the new facility was $1 million. The new building, named in honor of Dr. Harvey R. Gaylord, was ready for occupancy by 1927. Governor Smith made a very brief visit to the Institute October 28, 1927, quickly signed the Guest Book, and promptly left because of his fear that he would catch cancer.

Governor Smith had told the trustees as early as 1924 he wanted a better overview of what was happening at the Institute. *I do not know what is going on at the Institute and I do not know anybody in Albany that does.* In response, legislation was passed (LAWS OF NEW YORK 1926, Chapter 48, Article 18, February 2, 1926) placing the Institute under the jurisdiction of the New York State Department of Health, effective January 1, 1927. The administration and the Board of Trustees were not happy with this decision to place the Institute under the jurisdiction of the New York State Department of Health for fear of dealing with still another layer of bureaucracy. Their opposition proved futile.

In 1930 the Pathology Department logged pathological diagnoses from 12,000 patients submitted by physicians and dentists in New York State under the free Statewide Pathological Service. This free service was invaluable in the Institute's campaign for cancer control. And, by 1930, the Institute had an impressive *database* of complete medical histories on 10,399 patients treated at the hospital since 1913.

Dr. William H. Wehr began his thirty-seven-year career at Roswell Park in 1931; the same year he became one of the first physicians in the United States to use a radium bomb to treat cancer.

**3-15.**
Physicians dining room in Gaylord Building.

**3-16.**
Ladies' lunch room in the Gaylord Building. Mrs. Kelly, "Ma Kelly" to the staff and patients, served the best meals ever. She was Bob Stelley's (long time RPCI employee) grandmother.

In 1932 the State Health Department's Division of Cancer Control was created, with its headquarters at the Institute. Dr. Louis Kress was named Assistant Director of the new division. Education was one of the major activities of the Division of Cancer Control. The scope of the education program was reaching wide and far to disseminate cancer knowledge throughout the State. Cancer programs were initiated for the public, medical societies, high schools, colleges, and universities. The success of these programs was tremendous, and it was often difficult to fulfill the requests of the many groups wanting to know more about the cancer problem. Dr. Morton Levin, a trained public health officer, joined the staff of the Division of Cancer Control in 1936 to assist Dr. Kress, particularly to conduct statistical studies of 20,000 complete records in the Institute files.

Dr. Simpson and Dr. Alphonse Thibaudeau were principal organizers of the Western New York Branch of the American Association for Cancer Research in 1933. The Institute was well represented at the association's annual meetings at the Institute, where staff members presented many papers on original work. At that time, investigators made presentations on teratoma of the testes, on radium reactions in the bladder mucosa of patients treated for carcinoma of cervix, as well as a complete review of all cases of lung tumor treated at the Institute and their histological classification, metastases of squamous carcinoma, and the histology and embryology of lymph nodes.

The annual increase in the number of patients referred to the Institute for examination and treatment required rendering services to at least three times the number of patients the Institute was equipped to handle. While an attempt had been made to maintain high standards of service, it was increasingly difficult with a small staff and limited treatment facilities and bed capacity. The question at this time was whether the Institute would remain a research facility in which cases could be regulated so that all possibilities of known therapies could be carried out properly, or whether all cases would be accepted and as much as possible be done with the time and facilities available.

In 1933, and again in 1934, a hundred-bed hospital was requested, but was refused, since economic conditions in the Depression years had forced a reduction in statewide hospital services. All Institute appropriations were reduced to a minimum and staff members voluntarily took reductions in salary to keep the Institute functioning. (In looking back, these loyal members are to be greatly appreciated by all of us for keeping the Institute going!) The research program suffered as well, and this was the main reason that the renowned Coris left the Institute for a better academic research environment at Washington University in St. Louis. However, the accomplishments of Carl and Gerty Cori at Roswell Park had great impact on future research at the Institute and elsewhere. (See Appendix II, The Heritage of Carl and Gerty Cori at Roswell Park Cancer Institute.)

Mr. Millard C. Marsh, the Institute biologist, died in 1936. He had been on the staff since 1912, the director of the Biological Station at Springville since its inception in 1914, and had acquired international fame for his work in cancer research. In 1932 he was able to expand facilities at Springville, acquiring a brick facility to conduct mouse breeding and genetics research. He was one of the first to establish an inbred strain of cancer mice, and mice of the Marsh Strain were shipped to laboratories in all parts of the world. His passing was a distinct loss to cancer research and a very personal loss to his colleagues. Dr. William S. Murray replaced him as biologist. He came to the Institute from the Jackson Memorial Laboratory, Bar Harbor, Maine, and brought with him some valuable spontaneous strains of cancer mice.

**3-17.**

In 1932 Springville Laboratories gained a brick facility to conduct mouse breeding and mouse genetic research conducted by Mr. Marsh, who is standing at door of new facility.

**3-18.**

Assemblyman Frank Gugino was a staunch supporter of the Institute from 1930 to 1950. He was chairman of the Cancer Survey Commission that produced the report enabling us to obtain legislation for constructing the Simpson Building and postwar buildings of the Institute. We are very grateful for his efforts.

Also in 1936 Dr. Schreiner and Dr. Wehr reported five- and ten-year end results of treatment of cancer of the cervix uteri with radiation, gaining worldwide recognition for their outstanding, dependable data.

Dr. Burton Simpson, frustrated by his inability to convince the Governor and the New York State Department of Health of the need for expansion of physical facilities at the Institute, mobilized political support for a new hospital and other resources at the Institute by calling on the support of Mr. Edwin F. Jaeckle, chairman of the Erie County and New York State Republican Committees, Frank Gugino, State Assemblyman from the First Assembly District, and Senator Walter J. Mahoney.

Mr. Edwin F. Jaeckle, Mr. Frank Gugino, and Senator Walter J. Mahoney saw firsthand through visits to the Institute this increased patient activity without increased staffing and the need to revitalize the Institute's programs. Mr. Gugino introduced a bill in the State Assembly in 1937 and Senator Mahoney did the same in the State Senate to create the Cancer Survey Commission to study the cancer problem at the Institute and elsewhere in New York State, with reference to reorganizing the Division of Cancer Control in the State Health Department. Governor Herbert Lehman signed the bill into law and Mr. Gugino was appointed chairman of the Cancer Survey Commission. This Cancer Survey Commission was composed of two other assemblymen, three State senators, State Health Commissioner Dr. Edward S. Godfrey, Dr. James Ewing, director of Memorial Hospital in New York City, and Dr. Floyd S. Winslow, former president of the New York State Medical Society. The report of the Cancer Survey Commission not only influenced 1937 construction of the hospital, but the later expansion of the Institute after World War II during the Kress and the early part of the Moore administrations.

**3-19.**
Assemblyman F. Gugino conducted a statewide publicity campaign to seek funds for the Institute, front page headline in BUFFALO EVENING NEWS on February 7, 1937.

**3-20.**
The ALBANY EVENING NEWS on February 22, 1937, editorial cartoon generated by Assemblyman F. Gugino's campaign to seek funds to build the Simpson Building.

**3-21.**
An effective editorial cartoon in the BUFFALO EVENING NEWS on March 15, 1937, generated by Assemblyman F. Gugino's campaign to seek funds to build the Simpson Building.

**3-22.**
As a result of Assemblyman F. Gugino and Senator Walter Mahoney's efforts, bills were passed to build the Simpson Building.

**3-20.**

**3-21.**

We are much indebted to Mr. Gugino, Mr. Jaeckle, and Senator Mahoney for their persistence in keeping the Institute afloat. Their demand for funds for the Institute was chronicled in the BUFFALO EVENING NEWS on February 7, 1937, and the ALBANY EVENING NEWS on February 22, 1937. The BUFFALO EVENING NEWS article stated: *Their militant announcement arose out of denial of Governor Lehman and the State budget making authorities of the formal request made by Dr. Simpson for an appropriation for the hospital and purchase of x-ray machines.*

**3-22.**

In 1937 the hundred-bed hospital was finally approved, and land was purchased. The State legislature appropriated $510,000 for the building and new x-ray equipment including a 1,000,000-volt generator and other units for deep and superficial therapy. Since the amount did not cover the total cost, bed capacity was reduced to seventy-eight, although an annex for an enlarged Radiation Therapy Department was retained. All staff members now went on a full-time basis, and divisions were established for the various types of cancer, each headed by a specialist for the type of cancer. The bids for construction of the hospital were received April 14, 1938, and in 1940 the new hospital, called the Simpson Building in honor of Dr. Burton Simpson, was ready for occupancy.

The Institute admitted 3,645 patients in 1937, an increase of 8 percent over the previous year, and had close to 36,000 outpatient visits. Due to this increase in patient activity, and because the staff did not increase proportionately, a physician referral system for patients was started. Prior to this time, patients could simply walk into the hospital on their own. The Institute also hired its first telephone operators—Florence Griss and Emma Reuter—relieving the nursing staff of this duty.

Around this time, the Cancer Survey Commission, knowing how the Institute's facilities were still being taxed, was calling for additional State cancer hospitals, one in the central part and one in the eastern part of the State. This proposal had considerable support from legislators. However, opposition to a State system of cancer hospitals by numerous members of the medical profession was expressed on January 14, 1938, at a public Cancer Survey Commission hearing held at the Hotel Statler in Buffalo. The opposition was so fierce that the proposal was dropped.

In 1938, inspired by Dr. Morton Levin, the Institute began obtaining a history of tobacco usage from patients to study its relation to lung cancer. That same year, the Institute received a $33,333 bequest from the estate of Alfred H. Schoellkopf, known as the Schoellkopf Bequest Fund. Earnings from this fund still support research at the Institute.

From 1940 to 1942 the Institute was handicapped by the loss of staff members leaving for military service in World War II. Dr. Simpson served as president of the American Association for Cancer Research (AACR) in 1940 and Dr. Alphonse Thibaudeau served as vice president of the AACR in 1942.

**3-23.**
Emma Reuter at Simpson Building switchboard. She had a phenomenal memory and ability to seek out everyone on the staff.

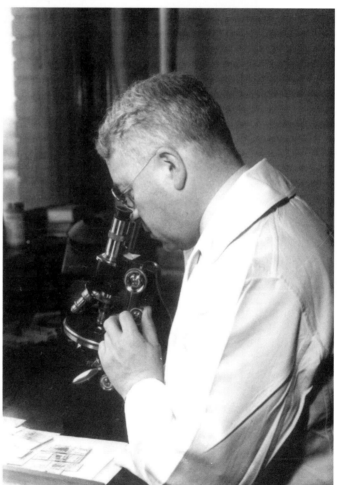

**3-24.**
Dr. A. A. Thibaudeau, the outstanding pathologist during the Simpson, Wehr, and Kress administrations (1924-1949). He died on April 6, 1949.

**4-1.**
Dr. William Wehr with
Mrs. Martha Wahl,
executive secretary for
many years for Dr. Wehr,
Dr. Kress, and Dr. Moore.

·····························1943·······

1945

In 1943 Dr. Simpson retired as the Institute's director and Dr. William H. Wehr, a graduate of the University of Buffalo Medical School, was appointed acting director. During his thirty-seven-year career (1931–1968), Dr. Wehr, who was popular and respected by all levels of the staff, saw the Institute grow from a few buildings with thirty beds for patients to a large research, treatment, and education complex. During his term as acting director, Dr. Wehr continued to serve as chief of Breast Surgery. He was influential in devising a program that brought medical students from the University of Buffalo to the Institute for formal oncology training. In 1937 he was the youngest member elected to the Board of Therapeutic Radiology and was an Honorary Life Member of the Erie County Unit, American Cancer Society.

Despite the wartime restrictions on civilian travel and a limited number of supportive staff due to the war, the Institute had a long waiting list of new and long-standing patients who needed treatment. The employment situation remained a problem due to many qualified personnel serving in the Armed Forces, but with Dr. Wehr's leadership and the devotion of the staff the entire Institute was able to carry on its mission.

At that time, treatment of cancer was divided into surgery, chemotherapy, and radiation. All types of surgery were available to cancer patients for eradication of the disease. Radium treatment was available in various forms. X-ray machines ranging from 45,000 to 1,000,000 volts were used for administration of x-ray treatment. There were newer forms of chemotherapy used in the treatment of cancer. However, the research program at the Institute still was curtailed due to a lack of suitable laboratory facilities and personnel. As it existed, the laboratories endeavoring to carry on limited research were overloaded with necessary work required by various clinical departments. Little or no time remained for research.

Lack of space was also a considerable hardship on patients. Many who should have been hospitalized during treatment were forced to remain ambulatory. This situation pointed to the pressing need for an enlarged Institute to facilitate the proper treatment of cancer patients. Fortunately, Dr. Wehr had a dedicated clinical staff to endure this situation: Dr. Walter Mattick, Dr. Charles Herger, Jr., Dr. Joseph O'Brien, Dr. George Sheehan, Dr. James Palmer, Dr. A. Thibaudeau, Dr. H. Traenkle, Dr. Harold Solomon, Mr. M. Reinhard, Mr. K. Buchwald, Dr. C. Cristy, Dr. Anthony Hey, Dr. H. Sauer, Dr. Walter Murphy, Dr. Trombetta, Dr. Erbacher, and others.

**4-2.**

Pictures of very dedicated senior staff taken in Dr. Wehr's administration. Many served in Simpson, Wehr, and even the early Moore administrations. They kept the Institute going during years of the Depression and during the war years under very difficult times. We owe them great respect for their dedication.

Dr. Wehr hoped that in the postwar period the necessary appropriations for expansion of the Institute would be provided for bed capacity and programs of academic research, clinical research, the treatment of cancer patients, and intensified educational programs. He sought the support of Mr. Edwin F. Jaeckle and Mr. Alfred H. Kirchhofer, managing editor of the BUFFALO EVENING NEWS. In 1943 Mr. Jaeckle and Mr. Kirchhofer used the report prepared by the Cancer Survey Commission, which was chaired by Assemblyman Gugino, to convince Governor Thomas E. Dewey that sweeping changes and expanded programs were needed at the Institute.

Governor Dewey appointed influential new members to the Institute's governing body, the Board of Visitors, and directed Dr. Edward S. Godfrey, Jr., New York State Health Commissioner, to give priority to redevelopment of the program for cancer control, and broadening the scope and upgraded operations of the Institute. The Board of Visitors has been active in directing the Institute in a positive way since that time. During the rest of his tenure, Dr. Godfrey's efforts were of major importance in carrying out Governor Dewey's intentions. Mr. Jaeckle and the Governor succeeded in counteracting an effort to transfer all of the State's cancer research from Buffalo to New York City.

In 1944 Mr. Alfred H. Kirchhofer, a good friend of Governor Dewey, was named to the Institute's Board of Visitors and helped to get the expanded facilities and programs for the Institute. Governor Dewey appointed him secretary of the Board in 1949 and Mr. Kirchhofer served most effectively the Institute in that role under six governors: Dewey, Harriman, Rockefeller, Wilson, Carey, and Cuomo, until his death in 1985. In 1979, then in his thirty-fifth year on the Board of Visitors, the Kirchhofer Conference Room on the fourth floor of the Main Building was opened in his honor. He never hesitated to intercede on our behalf.

**4-3.**

Many of the staff members at RPCI, dating back to the Gaylord, Simpson, Wehr, and early Kress administrations. The picture was taken of the staff in 1946 at a picnic on the grounds Biological Station at Springville. The staff was very congenial and often mixed for social occasions.

Floyd Meyer instructing technician on how to prepare radium for patient treatment.

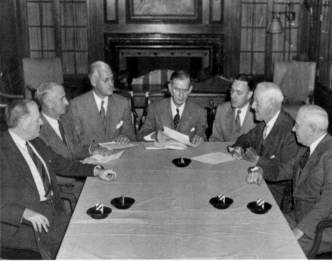

Miss Louise Merwin, superintendent of Nursing from 1924, resigned to get married and was replaced by Miss Glister as acting superintendent. She became ill and died in 1944, and was replaced by Acting Superintendent Miss Grace Scharlou.

In the State Senate at this time was one of the Institute's chief supporters, Majority Leader Senator Walter J. Mahoney, of Buffalo, later associate justice, Appellate Division of the State Supreme Court. In a letter dated August 20, 1971, to Dr. Gerald P. Murphy, Justice Mahoney stated, *My initial interest in the Institute came about as a result of a discussion with Assemblyman Frank Gugino in 1937 and Dr. William Wehr in 1943.* Senator Earl Brydges of Niagara Falls, Senator Mahoney's successor as majority leader of the State Senate, also maintained an active and cooperative interest in the Institute until his death in 1975. Without the support of these men, Institute programs would have been curtailed. Senate majority leaders before and after them (Perry Duryea, Warren Anderson, Ralph Marino and Joseph Bruno) as well as past and present Assembly leaders (Sheldon Silver, etc.) were equally supportive of the Institute.

Other delegates to the State legislature from Western New York to this day, assemblymen as well as senators, have been unremitting supporters of the Institute and its financial needs, recognizing in it an asset to Buffalo's scientific community, particularly, but not solely, for its contributions to cancer research. Indeed, this attitude is shared by all members of the legislature, irrespective of party, because the Institute's purposes are scientific and not political.

**4-5.**

The influential Board of Visitors appointed by Governor Dewey, left to right are: Dr. James B. Murphy, Dr. Fred S. Wetherall, Dr. Edward S. Godfrey, Mr. Alfred H. Kirchhofer (secretary), Dr. Walter L. Machemer, Dr. John T. Morton, and Dr. George W. Cottis (Chairman).

**5-1.**
Dr. Louis C. Kress,
Institute director,
operating in Cary
Pavilion. To the left
is the very influential
operating room nurse,
Miss Florence Kramer.

1945 . . . . . . .

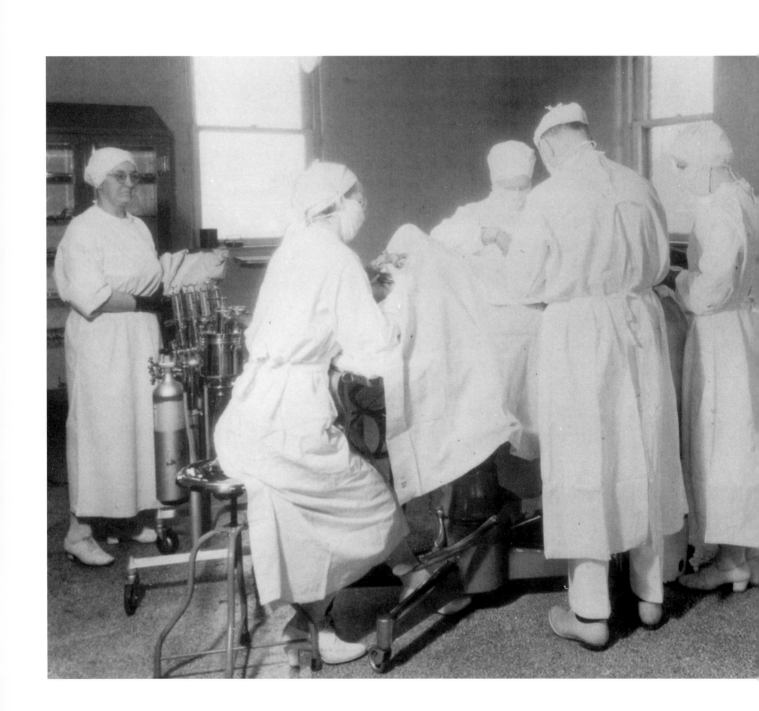

# Chapter 5

# Post–World War II Development: The Kress Years

In 1945 Dr. Louis C. Kress, a successful cancer surgeon who had previously become director of the New York State Health Department's Division of Cancer Control, was appointed fourth director of the Institute, replacing the acting director Dr. William H. Wehr. Mr. Kirchhofer, a close friend of Dr. Kress, was influential in getting Dr. Kress appointed director by Governor Dewey. Dr. Kress had received his medical degree from the University of Buffalo in 1918 and had done postgraduate work on bone tumors at Johns Hopkins University. He had been associated with the Institute since 1919, moving to Albany when the headquarters of the Division of Cancer Control were transferred there from Buffalo so that it could be centrally located for its statewide mission. His administrative team consisted of Senior Assistant Norman C. Sprickman and Dr. Joseph Hoffman, director of Cancer Research.

During his administration, the Institute embarked on an extensive educational program. Dr. Kress believed strongly that professional and public education was one of the best methods for controlling cancer. Through a close affiliation with the University of Buffalo School of Medicine and Dentistry, sophomore, junior, and senior medical students and senior dental students received instruction at the Institute. The U.S. Public Health Service sent physicians for training, enabling them to assume directorships of federal regional cancer offices. Buffalo General Hospital and Edward J. Meyer Memorial Hospital sent residents to the Institute for training. Organized groups of physicians and dentists were offered programs of one or more days. Postgraduate courses were conducted for nurses, and the staff participated in public education programs. For example, in 1945, the staff made sixty-nine presentations for lay audiences, two radio broadcasts, and eight exhibits at various meetings. In addition, the Institute's Medical and Scientific Library was reorganized under the direction of John M. Phelps, B.S.

Two outstanding physicians, Dr. Joseph MacManus and Dr. Leslie H. Backus, joined the staff enabling the Institute to broaden the scope of surgical treatment to thoracic, esophageal, and transthoracic surgeries, extirpation of the stomach and reconstructive procedures. Dr. Erwin Neter joined the staff and established a Department of Bacteriology in connection with the Department of Clinical Pathology.

**5-2.**

Residents and fellows trained at RPCI from 1950 to 1951. Since then we have trained over 4,000 physicians practicing in the U.S.A. and abroad. Back row, left to right: Drs. A. L. Bax, F. C. Marchetta, J. P. Haberlin, and S. M. Liana. Front row, left to right: P. G. Brendestsas, R. C. McCormick, and Edwin J. Lenahan.

Also in 1945 Miss Ethel Chandler, a superb nursing administrator, was appointed director of Nursing. (She was the last director of Nursing to live on campus, having an apartment in the Cary Pavilion.) She organized the growing Department of Nursing of sixty-one along the lines we see today with the assistance of Ruth Blair, assistant director of Nursing, and five prominent head nurses: Helene Nunn, Marian Render, Anna Aungst, Margaret Speno, and Grace Scharlou. Some of the staff nurses at this time were Isabelle Rutherford, Dorothy Usher, Grace Solomon, Marian Felex, Gertrude Saale, Theresa Kelly, Mae Culeton, Enid McCombs, Ellen McFadden, Eva Noles, Dorothy Zeh, Hazel Gustafsen, Genevieve Lake, Mary Ellen Baker, Elizabeth White, Alice McCarthy, Pauline DeLallo, Ann O'Brien, Violet Rinehold, Florence Kramer, Elizabeth Gaffney, Irene Astles, Mary Roth, Marie and Josephine Sova, Harriet Smith, Earl Osborne, Charles Newell, John Nagy, Cecelia Nowicki, Margaret Trager, Madelaine Prozellar, and Anna Schultz. All worked together for the good of the patients. In 1946 Anne Seniff was hired as the first nurse anesthetist to better enable the surgeons to do open thoracic procedures.

In 1946 Dr. J. Galvin Woodworth, a prominent dentist in Buffalo, suggested renaming the Institute in honor of its founder, so that Dr. Roswell Park's name might forever be associated with his greatest work. Assemblyman William Butler of the Third District introduced a bill in the legislature, along with a recommendation from the Board of Visitors. The bill passed and New York State Institute for the Study of Malignant Diseases became Roswell Park Memorial Institute.

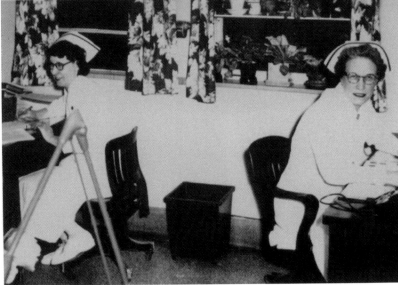

**5-3.**
Ethel Chandler, director of Nursing with assistant director of Nursing, Miss Ruth Blair.

**5-4.**
The loyal nurses' aides
served the patients
during the 1940s.

**5-5.**
Very dependable Red
Cross volunteers
served our patients
during the 1930s,
1940s and early 1950s.

Basic and clinical research program expansion
made it necessary to appoint a director of
Cancer Research in 1946. Dr. Joseph G. Hoffman,
a biophysicist and authority on biophysical characteristics of cells, was named to the position.
Before coming to Roswell Park, Dr. Hoffman had
worked on the Manhattan Project that led to the
development of the atom bomb. He was also one
of the first to study the effects of atomic radiation
on humans. At this time, research focused on
tumor growth studies, the effects of radiation on
transplantable tumors, the viral milk factor and
mammary tumors, the appearance of spontaneous
lymphatic tumors, genetic susceptibility to cancer, and the effect of androgen control therapy of
carcinoma of the prostate.

The Institute, with a staff of 268, admitted over
3,134 new patients a year, and outpatient visits
numbered over 41,000. It soon became evident
that the physical plant of the Institute was again
inadequate to provide modern medical care for
the ever-increasing number of patients being
referred and to expand the facilities for research
and teaching at the Institute.

**5-6.**
Dr. Joseph Hoffman at
the electron microscope.

**5-7.**
Dr. Joseph Hoffman with
senior staff members:
Dr. Donald Woernley
(seated), Dr. E. A.
Mirand (front), with
technicians in
laboratory in Gaylord
Building. Behind
Dr. Mirand is C. F.
Candee and next to
Dr. Hoffman is
Dolores Mickens.

**5-8.**
Ms. Betty Kress, the
Institute director's
daughter, who worked
in Dr. Donald Woernley's
biophysics laboratory.

**5-9.**
Technician working in
Dr. Woernley's laboratory.

**5-10.**
Mr. Andre Bulba
(standing), technician, in
one of early laboratories
in the 1950s.

**5-11.**
Business Office personnel
in early 1950s, left to
right are: _____, George
Romyak, Barbara Fauser,
William Intihar, _____,
Ann DuBois.

**5-8.**

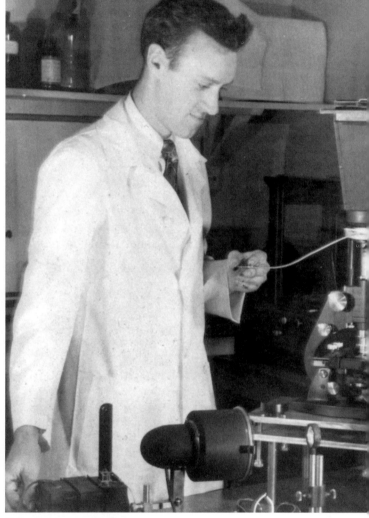

**5-9.**

**5-10.**

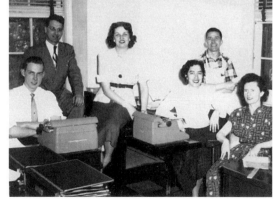

**5-11.**

In 1949 plans were completed for the construction of a $7,104,119 addition to the Institute. Money was allocated from the New York State Reconstruction Fund. Governor Dewey visited the Institute on October 27, 1950, to announce the expansion. A large group consisting of citizens of Buffalo, prominent educators, and representatives of all professional groups, as well as contractors attended the ceremony. Also, Dr. Louis C. Kress and several members of the senior staff, including Drs. William J. Staubitz, Walter T. Murphy, and Messrs. Donald M. Smith and Norman C. Spickman, attended. Mr. Alfred Kirchhofer, secretary of the Board of Visitors, introduced the Governor by saying that, *the new facility would be the fulfillment of a great humanitarian project started on its way by Governor Dewey.* He was referring to the Governor's instructions to Dr. Kress in 1945 to develop an *outstanding institution to deal with one of the terrible afflictions of mankind.*

In his remarks, Governor Dewey told the audience *that this is a moving occasion for me because two members of my family died of cancer.* He contrasted past frustrations with future hopes, saying*: When I became Governor, the State's only institution for care of cancer was so forgotten, so abandoned, that no new members of the Board of Visitors had been appointed for twenty-five years . . . a tragic abandonment of the State's obligations. Right then, I determined that we would change things. But with all our facilities mobilized for war, we could only plan and dream.* The first dirt was turned for the hospital addition on March 7, 1951.

He noted that in 1949 the Institute had provided 35,227 days of patient care and had performed over 423 major and 1,025 minor surgical procedures. He said that a new hospital would mean *better patient care, more accurate diagnosis, better rehabilitation, closer affiliation with the University of Buffalo, and improved training of medical students . . . as well as more extensive research equipment.*

**5-13.**
Staff in 1947 at farewell party for Ms. Lucy Alfano. Left to right: Helen Hornung, Ann DuBois, Barbara Fauser, Florence Maxwell, and Lucy Alfano. All were dedicated staff members during the Simpson, Wehr and early Moore administrations.

**5-15.**

The visit of Governor Thomas E. Dewey on October 27, 1950, announcing the $7,104,000 expansion of the hospital was a festive occasion. Senator Walter Mahoney, majority leader of the Senate, addresses the crowd at the occasion.

**5-14.**

Governor Thomas E. Dewey on October 27, 1950, visiting the Institute to announce with Dr. Kress the postwar construction project to expand the hospital. Left to right: _____, Mr. Edwin Jaeckle, Dr. Kress, Governor Dewey, Mr. Alfred H. Kirchhofer, Senator Walter T. Mahoney, Mayor T. Holling of Buffalo, and Assemblyman Frank Gugino. These men were all influential participants in getting the $7,104,000 for the hospital addition.

In 1950 Dr. Morton Levin was one of the first investigators to use epidemiology to study cancer when he reported on the relation between tobacco smoking and lung cancer, based on data accumulated at the Institute since 1938. In 1960 Dr. Levin urged the American Cancer Society to campaign against cigarette advertising and testified in a suit against Liggett & Myers Tobacco Company.

In 1951 Dr. Edwin A. Mirand was appointed to fill the vacancies created by departures of Dr. William Murray, director of the Biological Station at Springville, and Dr. Isadore Lubwin, director of the Biology Department on the main campus. (Dr. Mirand has been associated with the Institute since 1946, when he was a student.)

Dr. Kress died of a heart attack March 13, 1952, while in route to Rochester, New York, where he was to present a lecture that evening at the University of Rochester. Before leaving for Rochester, Dr. Kress had met for several hours with Dr. Mirand to discuss implementing the broad-based educational plan that Dr. Mirand had presented to the Board of Visitors on December 19, 1951. Dr. Morton Levin, assistant commissioner of the New York State Health Department, was named acting Institute director. However, Dr. Levin remained in Albany and Dr. William H. Wehr was again called on to conduct the day-to-day administration of the Institute, until Dr. George E. Moore's arrival as director. At this time the staff numbered 268.

**5-16.**

The actual first dirt is turned for $7,104,119 hospital addition to RPCI on March 7, 1951. Left to right: Mr. Edwin J. Hazard of William A. Berbusse, Jr., Contractors (pipe in mouth); Dr. William J. Staubitz, head of Urology Department; Dr. Walter T. Murphy, director of Radiology; Donald M. Smith, principal stationary engineer; Norman C. Sprickman, senior administrative assistant to Dr. Louis C. Kress, Institute director.

The broad concept of the Roswell Park Cancer Institute as a cancer research center of major significance and the model for the modern comprehensive cancer centers of today may be said to have risen at this time during the administration of Dr. Kress. On October 14, 1954, at the dedication of the new addition to the Institute, Governor Dewey acknowledged this by stating, *It is fitting that we pay special tribute to Dr. Louis C. Kress, director of the Institute, who contributed so much to the enormous development we are dedicating today. It is a tragedy that his death in 1952 prevented him from seeing the fruition of his dream, but I am grateful, as I know you are, that when he died, he knew that his dreams for a great research facility would be fulfilled.*

After the death of Dr. Kress, State Health Commissioner Dr. Herman E. Hilleboe brought forward the inspired idea of making the Institute not merely a hospital and outpatient clinic with incidental research projects, but instead a great institution devoted primarily to research. It was with this idea in mind that Dr. Hilleboe selected the next director of the Institute.

**5-18.**

Dr. and Mrs. Kress attending retirement party of Mrs. Kelly (Ma Kelly), beloved longtime dietitian and wonderful cook for the Institute. Dr. Walter Murphy is to her right. Ma Kelly was Mr. Robert Stelley's grandmother.

Smoking Machine for Mice

**6-1.**
Dr. Moore with
Governor Dewey and
NYS Commissioner
of Health Dr. Herman
Hilleboe. Dr. Moore
was very effective in his
relationships with the
"Trinity" (Governor's
staff, New York State
Commissioner of Health
and State Assembly,
and Senate), and for this
reason it contributed
effectively to our support
of programs during the
*Camelot Years*. Dr. Moore
showing experiments
on mice smoking
cigarettes to determine
the harmful effects of
tobacco smoking in
experimental animals.

1967

**6-2.**
Dr. Moore with Governor
Nelson Rockefeller and
Commissioner of Health
Dr. Herman Hilleboe.
Both men helped Dr.

Moore enthusiastically to
implement the research,
education and treatment
mission of the Institute.

George E. Moore, M.D., Ph.D., was appointed
fifth director of the Institute November 1, 1952.
Only thirty-two years of age, he was one of
the youngest men ever to receive a post of such
responsibility. He had been associate professor
of surgery, director of the Tumor Clinic, cancer
coordinator at the University of Minnesota
Medical School, and had already performed
unique studies in surgery and cancer research.
Dr. Moore served until 1967, when he was
appointed State Director of Public Health
Research. Under the stewardship of Dr. Moore,
who is regarded as the *Father of the Modern
Roswell Park Memorial Institute,* a tremendous
expansion program involving staff as well as
physical facilities evolved.

His administrative team during these years includ-
ed Assistant Institute Directors Dr. William H.
Wehr, Dr. Herschel C. Moss, Dr. James T. Grace,
Jr., Mr. Arthur Lepinot, and Mr. Frank L. Muddle,
Administrators Mr. Robert Goehle (business man-
ager), Mr. Russell Ketcham (director of personnel),
Mr. John Aungst (administrative assistant for spe-
cial projects), Dr. Robert K. Ausman (executive
director of Health Research, Inc.), Mr. John
Apostolakos (administrative director of Health
Research, Inc.), and Dr. Edwin A. Mirand, Dr.
Dorita Norton, Dr. Charles H. Ross and Dr. Julian
L. Ambrus (assistants to the director).

**6-3.**

One of the great accomplishments of Dr. Moore was to establish Health Research, Inc., to provide flexibility to the governance of the Institute. This organization enables the receipt of grants and other donations. Here is a meeting of Health Research, Inc., Board of Directors which included RPCI staff members, community leaders, and NYS Health Department representatives.

**6-4.**

Dr. George Moore extreme right with his Scientific Council, left to right: Dr. J. Grace, Dr. L. W. Law, Dr. R. D. Hotchkiss, Dr. C. C. Stock, Dr. G. E. Moore, Dr. C. A. Doan, Dr. R. Morgan, and Dr. S. Farber.

Dr. Moore must be given credit for his remarkable contributions as administrator, physician, and educator. During his administration, he nurtured and received superb political and programmatic support from Senator Majority Leader Walter Mahoney, Assembly Majority Leader Speno, Governors Dewey and Rockefeller, and New York State Commissioners of Health Drs. Herman E. Hilleboe and Hollis S. Ingraham to fulfill the goals of producing a modern comprehensive cancer center. These years, 1952 to 1967, are often referred to as the *Camelot Years* at the Institute.

Program expansion was fueled not only by State allocations but by increased grant funds available on the national level for cancer research. As a state facility, the Institute could not usually accept such funding. To enable the Institute to compete for funding of promising research, Dr. Moore urged formation of a non-profit corporation to receive gifts and research grants. On July 22, 1953, the Roswell Park Division of Health Research, Inc., was formed to fill this role. Mr. Robert C. Boggess, a full-time volunteer, was the first director of the new corporation. Now, more than $30 million is received each year in grants, contracts, and gifts from individuals, private foundations, and organizations such as the National Cancer Institute, the U.S. Public Health Service, the American Cancer Society, the Roswell Park Alliance, the National Science Foundation, the United Health Foundation, the American Heart Association, the John A. Hartford Foundation, Inc., the U.S. Department of Agriculture, the Atomic Energy Commission, and others.

Health Research Incorporated (HRI) was very important to Roswell Park during its explosive growth. It provided flexibility of planning buildings, hiring ancillary staff, appointing consultant architects such as Ted Lownie, and other assistance. The HRI Board at that time included: Mr. Alfred Kirchhofer, editor of the BUFFALO EVENING NEWS, Mr. Charles Diebold, a local bank president, and Dr. Herman E. Hilleboe, New York State commissioner of Health. The creative and energetic director of HRI was a former surgical resident, Dr. Robert K. Ausman.

Upon his arrival as Director, Dr. Moore moved swiftly to improve the scientific and clinical physical facilities of the campus. He had to assume, calling on the advice of his Scientific Council, the supervision of scientific programs and the $7,104,119 hospital addition started under the Kress administration as a postwar construction appropriation. The hospital addition was completed and the new building was dedicated on October 14, 1954, by Governor Dewey. In his remarks, Governor Dewey said: *It is a great privilege and honor to dedicate this hospital today to the hope that building on the past, the research performed will speed the day when the science of medicine can say cancer, this enemy, too, has been conquered.* The Governor was joined on the program by Dr. Herman E. Hilleboe, Dr. Moore, Dr. Julian Park (son of the founder of the Institute), Dr. Morton Levin, Dr. Charles S. Cameron of the American Cancer Society, Dr. Michael J. Kopac, Dr. Leonard Scheele, United States surgeon general, and Dr. Renato J. Azzari of the New York State Medical Society. Dr. Scheele recalled his coming to the Institute in 1937 as part of his training making friendships with Drs. Simpson and Kress and many members of the staff. He mentioned Roswell Park was one of the first institutions that opened its doors in the late 1930s to aid the National Cancer Institute in developing their seminal epidemiologic study of cancer.

The Seames Catering Company building at 177 High Street was purchased in 1955 to provide space for chemical and pharmacological laboratories and for the maintenance of small animals. The building was named the Boggess Laboratories in honor of Robert C. Boggess. On October 4, 1971, the Boggess Laboratories were destroyed by a fire that had spread from an adjacent privately-owned building.

6-6.
Miss Cecelia Nowicki at
the Official Entrance to
RPCI bidding patient
farewell (1960).

**6-7.**
Volunteer serves patient
free coffee in the lobby
of the Hospital.

**6-8.**
The duck pond in the
lobby of the Hospital
was a favorite of patients
and visitors.

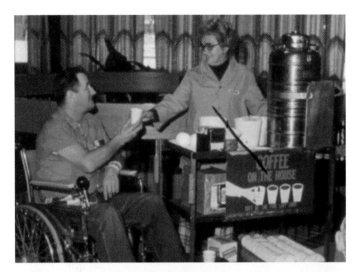

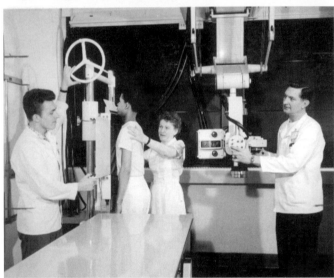

**6-9.**
Diagnostic x-ray staff
in the new Hospital in
early 1960.

**6-10.**
Dr. Donald Parsons
preparing patient for
x-ray treatment in the
new Hospital.

**6-11.**
The Seames Catering
Building was remodeled
to become Boggess
Laboratories.

The New Aerial Theatre building at 185 High
Street was purchased at this time by Health
Research, Inc., to provide additional laboratory
and storage facilities and space for housing small
animals. This was called the Gratwick Building
for the next few years, to perpetuate the name in
the Institute complex, until construction on the
Gratwick Basic Science Building was completed.
The Mergenhagen Candy Company building at
187 High Street was purchased in 1959 to provide space for research on oncogenic viruses.
This building became the Clowes Building in
honor of Dr. George H. A. Clowes.

The Springville Biological Laboratories needed
updated facilities. Many of the buildings were
built before World War I and shortly thereafter.
Consequently, a $1 million research building
funded by State funds was completed on the
Springville campus in 1959. This building was
used for studies by Dr. Leonell C. Strong and
his staff involving mouse cancer genetics, studies
on aging, and long-term irradiation effects on
a variety of mammals.

Promising work at the Institute made a program
of almost continuous expansion necessary. The
Institute's $5,600,000 Basic Science Building,
placed on the site of the original Gratwick
Research Laboratory and the Cary Pavilion, was
dedicated on June 17, 1960, and the final stage
of its construction was completed in September
1961. The seven-story building contained more
than fifty laboratories for research in chemistry,
biology, physics, and experimental animal
surgery; its medical library contained close
to 30,000 volumes.

**6-12.**
The New Aerial Theatre
was named temporarily
the Gratwick Building.

**6-13.**
Mergehagen Candy Company Building was remodeled and named Clowes Building.

**6-16.**
The original Gratwick Research Laboratory was demolished to put up the new Gratwick Basic Science Building.

**6-14.**
This is what the buildings look like after remodeling of the New Aerial Theatre and Mergehagen Candy Company Building.

**6-15.**
Aerial view of Springville Laboratories showing new facilities to the campus.

**6-17.**
New Gratwick Basic Science Building was placed on the site of the original Gratwick Research Laboratory and Cary Pavilion.

**6-18.**
The new autoclave was one of the many important features in Gratwick Basic Science Building. The building has more than fifty laboratories. Programs carried out in the new structure include studies in such fields as physics, neurophysiology, steroid chemistry, radiobiology, biochemistry, experimental biology, and experimental pathology.

**6-19.**
Modern laboratory facilities in the Gratwick Basic Science Building.

The Batt Heating Company building, 955 Michigan Avenue at the corner of Carlton Street, was acquired in 1961 and named for Dr. Louis C. Kress, the fourth Director of the Institute. Other buildings had their names changed as well. The Mergenhagen Candy Company Building, which had been named the Clowes Building, had always been known as the Mergenhagen Building. Accordingly, the designation of the Mergenhagen Building was made official, and the former New Aerial Theatre building, which had been called the Gratwick Building, but had never been consistently known by any single designation, was renamed the Clowes Building. The second change made it possible to add Gratwick to the name of the Basic Science Building, so that the latter is now officially the Gratwick Basic Science Building. These renamings finally brought order to the confusion, and hence the three buildings could be listed definitively as follows: Gratwick Basic Science Building (115 High Street); Clowes Building (185 High Street); and Mergenhagen Building (187 High Street).

Institute staff members required large numbers of mice reared under acceptable genetic and hygienic standards to conduct research. A $281,415 U.S. Public Health Service Grant was awarded in 1960 to provide such a facility. The grant money permitted the purchase of farm land and construction of a 14,884-square foot building at 2879 Clinton Street in West Seneca.

The facility opened in late 1961 under the scientific direction of Drs. Theodore Hauschka and Edwin A. Mirand. At its operational peak, the West Seneca Laboratories produced more than 500,000 inbred and random-bred mice annually for the Institute and other research laboratories in the United States and abroad. The West Seneca Laboratories ceased operation in October 1991.

**6-20.**
Batt Heating Company
Building located on
Carlton Street and
Michigan Avenue.

**6-21.**
Batt Heating Company
Building remodeled to
become Kress Building.

**6-22.**
The West Seneca
Laboratories located
at 2879 Clinton Street.

**6-23.**
Tower Apartment
Building, located
across from the Hospital,
provided housing for
residents, staff and for
Health Research, Inc.,
employees.

To ease a critical housing shortage for students, resident physicians, and other staff members, construction began on a $1.4 million residence building at Elm and Carlton Streets in 1960. This ninety-one-unit building, completed in 1962, also provided office space for Institute and Health Research, Inc., functions. Originally called the Tower Apartments, it became known as Roswell Park Apartments, and was owned by the Roswell Park Housing Co., Inc., a non-profit, membership corporation. The Roswell Park Apartments was razed in 1994 as part of the $241.5 million Major Modernization Project. Dr. Moore had been inspirational in establishing around the Institute a housing and renewal authority to develop *low income* housing. He personally designed unique units, later adapted by the Baptist Church, and the construction of the Carlton House Nursing Home, which was later purchased by Roswell Park in 1974.

A Cancer Clinical Research Center, consisting of laboratories and facilities for sixteen patients, was constructed in 1962 in the east wing of the fourth floor of the Institute's hospital. Initially financed by a seven-year, $2.6 million U.S. Public Health Service Grant, it brought together laboratory research and clinical studies dealing with the effects of diet and drugs on cancer, particularly leukemia. The Center was originally organized under the direction of Dr. James F. Holland, Chief of the Department of Medicine A.

**6-24.**
Dr. Moore pointing
out his community
development plan around
the Institute to Governor
Nelson Rockefeller.

**6-25.**
Cell & Virus Building
located on High Street
was completed in 1965.

The Wehr Building, adjacent to the rear of the Clowes and Mergenhagen buildings, was constructed in 1962, at a cost of $100,000. The Wehr Building provided additional laboratory space and animal housing, and was named in honor of Dr. William H. Wehr, then in his thirty-first year of service to the Institute.

Construction began on the seven-story Cell & Virus Building at the corner of Elm and High Streets in 1963, to accommodate particularly our active viral carcinogenesis program. The $4.3 million project, funded by the State and by the U.S. Public Health Service, was completed in 1965, and dedicated by Governor Nelson A. Rockefeller, New York State Health Commissioner Dr. Hollis S. Ingraham, and other dignitaries. The building is still devoted to research activities in virology, cell culture, biochemistry, endocrinology, and germ-free biology.

In his remarks, Governor Rockefeller said: *Roswell Park Memorial Institute has become a mecca of hope for the thousands of patients treated here and a bright beacon to cancer fighters the world over who study here.*

**6-26.**
Governor Nelson
Rockefeller touring
Cell & Virus Building
after dedication in 1965.

The Center for Crystallographic Research was completed in 1965 at a cost of $400,000 in State and Health Research funds. Located on Michigan Avenue next to the Kress Building, the new facility was devoted to the branch of science concerned with arrangements of atoms in substances, and how the properties of the substances are related to these arrangements. The Center at that time was the only one of its kind in the United States.

In October 1965, the Institute's federally-funded General Clinical Research Center (GCRC) was organized under the direction of Dr. James T. Grace, Jr. The laboratories were set up in the 2 West area of the hospital building, with administrative offices on the fifth floor. Patients were first admitted to the GCRC in July 1966. The 2 West area was completely remodeled in the course of the next few months, and the GCRC reopened there in March 1967. The GCRC was unique among the Institute's clinical services because it was a combined medical and surgical unit which accepted patients with diseases other than cancer for study. The GCRC was designed, even more than most Institute facilities, to apply the results of chemical and pharmacological studies to clinical studies in the same unit.

A $1,850,000 Power Plant located next to the Cell & Virus Building was completed to serve the entire Roswell Park complex in 1966.

Dr. Moore always had big plans for the Institute, including the formation of a Comprehensive Research Center which would include a Cardiovascular Research Center, Brain Institute, Genetics Center, and Renal Transplant & Dialysis Center. His proposal was justifiably supported by a number of existing research studies. Preliminary discussions were held in Buffalo and Albany, but an adversarial political posture by representatives from other domains in the State, a weakening of the political clout from Western New York, the financial problems of Health Research, Inc., and little interest by changing administrations of the University of Buffalo and its Medical School caused it to *die aborning*.

**6-28.**

Dr. Moore attracted national and international members of the biomedical community. Here Surgeon General Stewart visited the Institute. This picture shows senior staff members at that time from left to right: Mr. R. Case, Mr. R. Ketcham, Dr. R. Vincent, Dr. Hoffmeister, Dr. E. Klein, Dr. M. Bender, Dr. Ralph Jones, Dr. F. Marchetta, Dr. J. Cortner, Dr. J. Horoszewicz, Dr. E. Mirand, Dr. C. Nichol, Dr. D. Pressman, Dr. J. Pickren, Dr. T. Dao, and Dr. Woodruff. Dr. Moore in center with Surgeon General Stewart.

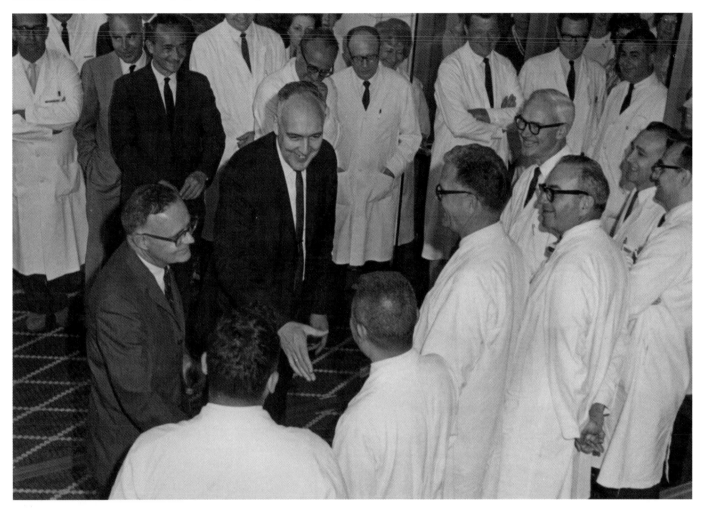

**6-29.**

Dr. Moore with Surgeon General Dr. Stewart and from left to right: Mayor Frank Sedita of Buffalo, Congressman William Miller, Dr. G. Moore, Congressman T. Dulski, and Dr. Stewart. Mayor Sedita giving the Surgeon General a Buffalo Bison.

**6-30.**

Dr. Moore attracted outstanding members to the senior staff: Dr. Leonell Strong from Yale School of Medicine to head Springville Laboratories. He was an authority on mouse genetics. Here with Dr. Mirand (right) in academic attire.

Because of its superb facilities and Dr. Moore's leadership, Roswell Park was able to attract government officials in the biomedical field and staff specialists from some of the finest scientific institutions in the world. Among these was Dr. Leonell C. Strong, dean of the cancer geneticists in the United States. Dr. Strong came to the Institute from the Yale University School of Medicine and gained a reputation worldwide as the originator of a number of strains of mice used in cancer research. Also appointed was Dr. Robert Guthrie from the University of Minnesota, who discovered the PKU Test for phenylketonuria. The Guthrie Test is routinely given to newborn babies.

Dr. Moore also was able to recruit two outstanding anesthesiologists—Drs. James Elam and Elwyn S. Brown, and a renowned researcher, Dr. Werner K. Noel. Their work at this time, in collaboration with the physiologist Dr. Werner K. Noel, on mechanical ventilation and artificial respiration revolutionized the field of anesthesiology. They also were the first to describe the use of mouth-to-mouth respiration.

A Department of Urology was established in 1953 and Dr. William J. Staubitz, principal cancer urologist, became its first chief.

The Institute's research program took a major step forward in 1954, when Dr. David Pressman was recruited from Sloan-Kettering Institute and appointed director of the Biochemistry Department. Dr. Pressman pioneered the first studies on the use of radiolabeled antibodies to localize tumors. He and his colleagues also gained worldwide recognition for their research on the structural characterization of antibodies and the application of antibodies to defining surface antigens, including those found on neoplastic cells.

Also in 1956, Dr. Donald P. Pinkel founded the Department of Pediatrics and organized the first multi-institutional group (Acute Leukemia Group B) for the study of cancer.

Dr. James T. Grace, Jr., joined the Institute staff in 1957 as associate chief of the Department of Gastrointestinal Surgery, coming to Buffalo from the Vanderbilt School of Medicine. The following year, he became chief of the Gastrointestinal and Soft Tissue Surgical Services, and the United States Junior Chamber of Commerce named him one of the nation's ten outstanding young men of the year. Dr. Grace was the first Buffalonian to be thus designated. The James T. Grace, Jr., Park, located behind the Cancer Cell Center, was dedicated by the City of Buffalo in 1977.

**6-31.**
Dr. James Grace
instructing a trainee
on how to use a blood
pipette to obtain a
blood sample on a rat.

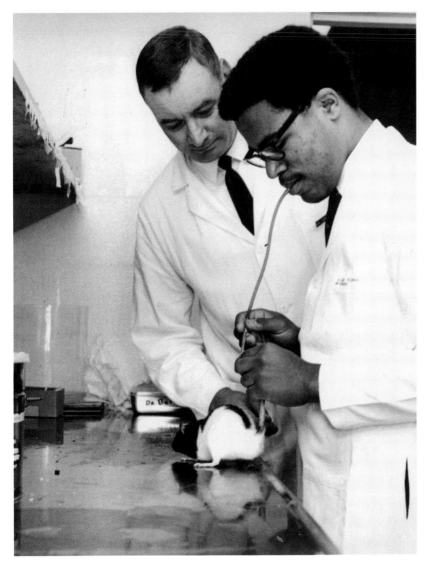

The late 1950s and early 1960s were years of ferment, a time of rapid and impressive growth, with a staff and trainees of over 2,500, as a result of Dr. Moore's keen direction. Dr. Moore believed in hiring young, working physicians and scientists to head departments. During this period, the Institute gained a number of gifted and highly productive physicians (Drs. Merrill A. Bender, James Holland, Avery A. Sandberg, Robert Tarail, D. Perese, Guy Owens, Franz Lessmann, Joseph Sokal, John Pickren, John Graham, Arnold Mittelman, Edith Sproul, U. Kim, J. F. Gaeta, Lenore Simpson, F. R. Sheehan, John Ingall, Nancy Stubbe, Kenneth Eckert, George Blackman, L. Belmusto, J. D. Bartels, J. C. Patterson, and others) and scientists (Drs. David Pressman, Oliver Roholt, Bernard Amos, Alfred Nisonoff, Thomas Shows, Gabor Markus, Jun Minowada, Charles Nichol, Theda Bennett, Eugene Day, William F. McLimans, Donald Parsons, Monte Blau, Enrico Mihich, Saxon Graham, Abraham Lilienfeld, Irwin Bross, Morton L. Levin, Ruth Graham, L. E. Blumenson, R. Priore, Fred Bock, Joseph DiPaolo, Olga Pierucci, and others) who enhanced the Institute's worldwide reputation with their innovative and constructive approach to cancer research and treatment. Most of them are now known far beyond the confines of the Institute for the quality and creativity of their work. Also, the interaction between the clinicians and scientists was intense.

In 1958, to accommodate many of the appointees who desired union affiliation, the first chapter of the Civil Service Employees Association (CSEA) was organized at the Institute. The parent organization, founded in 1910, consisted of about 130,000 employees of the State of New York and about 80,000 employees of various other governmental units, mostly geographical subdivisions of New York State. About 1,000 State employees were members of the first chapter at Roswell Park. A second chapter was organized in 1967 for about 180 employees of Health Research, Inc.

**6-32.**
Dr. James Holland, one
of the chiefs of Medicine,
contributed substantially
to chemotherapy of
leukemia.

**6-33.**
Dr. Avery Sandberg with
student Jeffrey Hoffman.

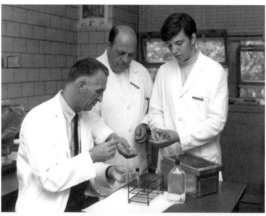

**6-34.**
Dr. Theda Bennett
established a complete
laboratory for
investigators of water
and electrolyte
metabolism under
Dr. Robert Tarail, chief
of Clinical Laboratories
and Metabolism.

**6-35.**
Dr. Fred Rosen, Dr. E. A.
Mirand, Dr. John Pickren,
and Dr. Joseph Sokal.

**6-36.**
Dr. Alan Grossberg,
immunochemist, with
graduate student
Jimmy Klostergaard.

**6-37.**
Dr. Charles Nichol
from Yale University,
Director of Department
of Experimental
Therapeutics—an authori-
ty on anticancer drugs.

**6-38.**
Dr. Donald Parsons
shows student how
to operate electron
microscope.

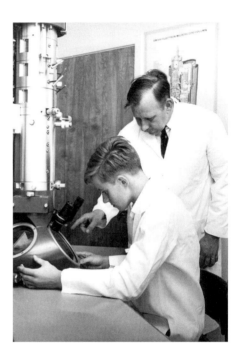

**6-39.**
Dr. Guy Owens was
appointed chief of
Neurosurgery, replacing
Dr. Perese who left for
private practice. Dr.
Owens later left for a VA
Hospital in Connecticut
where Dr. Grace was
taken after his serious
car accident and later
succumbed, never
regaining consciousness.

**6-40.**
Dr. Eugene Day,
immunochemist, in Dr.
Pressman's Department.

**6-41.**
Dr. Charles Ross of
Thoracic Department
reviewing patient
records with his staff
and clinical trainees.

**6-42.**
Dr. Jacob Furth, director
of Experimental
Pathology.

**6-43.**
Dr. David Harker
(right) from Polytechnic
Institute of Brooklyn,
director of Biophysics,
world authority in
crystallography.

Dr. Theodore Hauschka, well-known scientist from Fox Chase Cancer Center in Philadelphia, became Director of the Department of Experimental Biology. Two world-renowned scientists joined the Institute in 1959, Dr. Jacob Furth as director of Experimental Pathology, and Dr. David Harker, who brought with him his research team (Dr. Dorita Norton) from the Polytechnic Institute of Brooklyn, as director of Biophysics.

Also in 1961, Dr. Donald S. Pinkel left the Pediatrics Department to become director of the St. Jude Children's Research Hospital in Memphis Tennessee. Dr. Lucius Sinks replaced Dr. Pinkel.

Mr. Charles E. Martin became the director of Nursing in 1962, replacing Miss Mary Crook, who resigned to marry Dr. John Mitchell.

In 1964 Dr. Leonard Weiss, cell physiologist, left the Strangeways Research Laboratory in Cambridge, England, to become director of the Institute's Department of Experimental Pathology. Under his direction, the Department performed extensive research on the relation of cell surface properties to the development of cancer.

In 1965 Dr. Julian L. Ambrus, who, along with his wife Dr. Clara Ambrus, had been leading research investigators in the Institute's Department of Experimental Biology for a number of years, was made head of the Institute's Biological Station at Springville, replacing Dr. Leonell Strong who retired in 1964. The facility was soon renamed the Springville Laboratories. Under Dr. Ambrus' direction, this facility was dedicated to clinically-related and basic research studies that could be performed more satisfactorily in a country setting than in the city.

Dr. David Harker was named director of the Crystallography Center at its inception. Two years later, he and his staff successfully determined the intricate molecular structure of the enzyme ribonu-clease, an achievement that took sixteen years and cost a total of $2 million. Their work complement-ed that of other scientists leading to the production of synthetic enzymes in other laboratories across the country.

**6-44.**
Dr. Theodore Hauschka
from Fox Chase Cancer
Center, an authority
on transplantation
and genetics and
chromosomal aberrations
of tumors, and director
of Experimental Biology.

**6-45.**

Dr. George Moore had an excellent relationship with the staff at all levels. He actively communicated with them. Here in 1967 he is with RPCI Humboldt YMCA volleyball team. Standing: Dr. G. E. Moore, Charles Bishop, Ron Wooford, and Peter Uberschaer. Kneeling: Phillip Taylor, Steve Green, and Leon Hall. Missing is Harry Halberslaben.

Another important event in 1965 was the recruitment of Dr. Michael Laskowski, who was named head of the Enzymology Section of the Department of Experimental Therapeutics and began studies of nucleolytic enzymes, the substances that unravel nucleic acids. In 1966 Dr. Laskowski was granted the second lifetime research professorship ever awarded by the American Cancer Society.

Dr. Moore also believed in integration of the Institute long before it became popular. When Dr. Moore arrived at Roswell Park, there was only one staff member of African-American descent, and she was harassed by her peers. When he resigned in 1967, 18 percent of the staff was of African-American descent. The Institute conducted evening classes which aided in preparing employees for advancement. A volleyball team served to provide an informal forum for communication between the director and the staff, and aided in settling many problems without official recognition. The team also won the State B championship in successive years.

To acknowledge the dedication of the staff, the 25-Year Club was organized to honor employees who had worked for the Institute for at least twenty-five years.

The scientific excellence at the Institute at this time has been documented by a number of accomplishments that still have tremendous impact today. A few examples follow.

Two important tissue culture media were developed at this time which have had enormous impact on biological and pharmacological cell research around the world. Dr. George E. Moore and colleagues developed RPMI 1640. The RPMI 1640 is still the most-sold medium in the world over thirty years later. Dr. Maire Hakala, a scientist in the Experimental Therapeutics Department, provided the basis for the HAT (Hypoxanthine, Aminopterin and Thymidine) medium which has been essential to modern studies in molecular biology and the hybridoma technology for monoclonal antibody production. Dr. Moore developed a huge complex culture plant especially to grow human B-lymphoid cell lines. His approach was successfully adopted as a model by cell plant centers in England and Japan.

**6-46.**

25-Year Club gathering in 1965 showing staff members Ellen McFadden, Eugene Burke, Helen Langerman, Dr. Wehr, Russell Ketcham, Cecelia Nowicki, Edward Kaczmarek, Minerva Brennan, Bill Payne, Dr. Candee, etc.

Dr. Moore and his staff maintained that experimental studies supported the thesis that perhaps autochothonous cultured B-lymphoid cells could be used as cellular therapy for malignancies—*adoptive immunotherapy.* It was also suggested that in the future cultured human cells could produce valuable cell products and even be used therapeutically against drug resistant bacteria (leprosy), fungi, and parasites. The first therapeutic application of human cells was performed by Dr. Moore and staff on January 19, 1969, in a physician with malignant melanoma. Although partial regressions were spectacular, he was not convinced of the specificity of the cell interactions, so back to the laboratory they went. However, over the next twenty years, adoptive immunotherapy became popular.

Dr. Moore's team established a melanoma cell line RPMI 7932 in February 1970 and determined a method to produce large amounts of plasminogen activator. Huge amounts of this cell line were cultured and the enzyme was used to treat coronary thrombi. Genentech patented a transfection of the genome for clinical use.

At this time, through Dr. Moore's impetus, great emphasis was placed on the culture of normal human leukocytes and leukocyte cultures from patients with leukemia, lymphoma, and myeloma. Those researchers working with Dr. Moore included Drs. R. Gerner, Jun Minowada, J. L. Glick, Audrey Fjelde, B. W. Papermaster, and William McLimans.

Also at this time, other investigators were conducting innovative research projects, including: Dr. Julius Horosewicz, Dr. V. C. Dunkel, Dr. L. Avila, Dr. James T. Grace, Jr., Dr. Y. Hinuma, and Dr. T. Osato on mycoplasmas and human leukemia and lymphoma; Dr. W. H. Munyon, on thymidase kinase activity in Herpes Simplex Virus; Dr. William A. Carter and his staff, on the purification of mouse and human interferons; Dr. Leonard Weiss, on the biophysical aspects of metastases; Dr. David Harker, on the biological importance of the shapes of biomolecules, for example, the structure of ribonuclease; Dr. Fred G. Bock, on the development of less carcinogenic cigarettes; Dr. Theodore Hauschka, on chromosome aberations and tumor growth; Dr. Kenneth Paigen, on the molecular genetics of beta-glucoronidase; and Dr. Fred Rosen, on the glucocorticoid receptors in lymphoid tissues.

Dr. Moore urged Dr. Mirand to confirm the controversial studies of Dr. S. E. Stewart and Dr. Bernice Eddy on the polyoma virus. The Institute's confirmation of these published studies led to the second phase of national and international studies on the role of viruses in cancer, as well as a program at Roswell Park. Prior to this, the role of viruses in cancer was largely ignored, despite the early work at the Institute, and by Dr. Peyton Rous at the Rockefeller Institute, Dr. F. Duran-Reynals, Dr. J. J. Bittner, Dr. C. Friend and others supporting this concept.

Chemotherapy research took a major step forward in 1956 and thereafter, when the Department of Experimental Therapeutics became an administrative entity under Dr. Charles Nichol, and later under Dr. Enrico Mihich. From the initial group of twenty-two employees, the department has grown today to become the largest research unit at the Institute, with a staff of 137 located in the Grace Cancer Drug Center.

Research in the Department of Experimental Therapeutics under Drs. Nichol and Mihich has been conducted in four general areas, namely: (a) the development and study of new drugs and treatments; (b) the study of basic aspects of cell metabolism and function and their regulation that may provide ideas leading to the development of new types of compounds and treatments, particularly studies of control mechanisms in cancer cells, such as signal transduction, gene transcription and cell cycle control which may provide new sites for intervention; (c) preclinical study of biochemical and pharmacological basis for selective toxicity of anticancer drugs and treatments and of means to increase the antitumor selectivity of these treatments; and (d) translational clinical study (in close cooperation with clinical departments) of the pharmacological and biochemical determinants of drug action and means to optimize the use of known and new agents alone and in combination.

Dr. Moore initiated a major effort to reduce the carnage from tobacco use. Dr. Morton Levin, a former assistant commissioner of the Department of Health, acting Institute director in 1952, and subsequently a staff member, was co-author of one of the seminal reports on smoking and cancer in 1950. A Tobacco Committee was formed at the Institute by Dr. Moore to study education, epidemiology, carcinogenesis, tobacco substitutes, and legislation on tobacco and cancer.

One must remember that forty years ago adversarial actions against anyone stating that cigarette smoking was dangerous were swift and punitive. Many physicians doubted the evidence of lung cancer causation and indeed a major medical association had stock in tobacco companies and accepted money from the Tobacco Institute to support *relevant* research. The accusations of zealot, maniac bias, moralistic compulsion, etc., were common. The Roswell Park staff resolved to limit any and all releases to factual data and proposed extensive carcinogenic studies. Biological studies included quantitation of smoke condensate (tar) from various brands of filtered and non-filtered cigarettes, assays by painting the skin of mice with smoke tar, and a search for active smoke fractions.

Dr. Moore felt that to keep pace with research on the relation of tobacco smoking and cancer, a former Air Force Base in Orchard Park, New York, should be acquired by Health Research in the summer of 1964 as surplus property. Its major buildings were converted to laboratories and a greenhouse was added. The staff at the Orchard Park Laboratories, under the direction of Dr. Fred G. Bock, performed research on the role of tobacco in causing cancer. A number of acres of farmland were devoted to experimental crops in the hope of developing a *safe*—less carcinogenic—cigarette.

6-47.
Dr. Moore with technician removing tar from various brands of cigarettes for study for tumor producing effects.

**6-48.**
Aerial view of Orchard Park Laboratories.

**6-49.**
Harvested tobacco leaves grown on our farm at Orchard Park Laboratories.

**6-50.**
A rogue's gallery of famous people who advertised cigarettes and then developed lung cancer.

Probably the most dramatic program was the collection of tobacco seedlings from Maryland and the successful growth of a superb harvest of tobacco leaves from our *farm* in Orchard Park. One purpose was the manufacture of cigarettes with tobacco unexposed to insecticides and growth hormones and without a great number of additives used in commercially produced cigarettes. Dr. Bock determined that the carcinogenicity of the Roswell Park brand was essentially the same as commercial cigarettes. Cigarettes were also made from lettuce, sugar beets, chard, and tree leaves. Temporary greenhouses were built on the roof of the Institute and sometimes the auditorium was festooned with lines of drying leaves!

For the first time, cigarette smoking was associated with bladder cancer. The epidemiological study was directed by the prominent Dr. Abraham Lilienfeld from the Department of Biostatistics.

Educational programs were developed for adults and schoolchildren. Preventive programs were held in the evening. Cartoon and display contests were held. A rogue's gallery of famous people who advertised cigarettes and then developed lung cancer graced the main corridor. Tobacco company representatives threatened to sue Roswell Park. They also mounted many serious pressures on staff members and the Institute.

Dr. Moore was involved in several legal cases and twice was threatened with citation for contempt of Congress during testimony before Congressional Committees.

In retrospect, the Roswell Park research team played a significant role and deserves major credit for the recent major reversal of social and medical acceptance of the dangers of smoking and, in 1964, U.S. Surgeon General Dr. Luther Terry was successful in having health warnings put on tobacco product packaging.

Other studies at the Orchard Park Laboratories dealt with genetic control of plant differentiation and with the interaction of plant hormones with genetic systems.

In the early 1960s, the initial promise of chemotherapy as a cancer treatment was becoming a reality, particularly for patients with leukemia. However, chemotherapy decreased the patient's ability to produce blood platelets and lifesaving platelet transfusions were needed. To help meet this critical need for platelets, Dr. Elias Cohen started the first voluntary Plasmapheresis Donor Center for blood platelet collection at the Institute in 1964, with contract support from the Acute Leukemia Task Force of the National Cancer Institute.

The role of the senior staff in helping establish and nurture the American Association for Cancer Research (AACR) was as important as their role in the early years of the Institute. The AACR is a prestigious scientific organization known worldwide. Early staff members, Drs. Harvey R. Gaylord and George H. A. Clowes were founding members of the organization who helped establish the AACR on May 7 and 8, 1907. National meetings of the AACR were held in Buffalo on April 15, 1908, April 11, 1911, and April 17, 1924. The following members of our early staff and current staff have been recognized by their peers to be officers of the AACR: Dr. Harvey R. Gaylord, secretary, 1907–1909, president, 1909–10 and 1916–17, vice president, 1910–11; Dr. Leo Loeb, president, 1911–12; Dr. Cary N. Calkins, president, 1913–14; Dr. Burton T. Simpson, president, 1926–27, 1940–41; Mr. Millard C. Marsh, vice president, 1933–34, president, 1934–35, secretary-treasurer, 1935–36; Dr. Alphonse A. Thibaudeau, secretary-treasurer, 1936–42, vice president, 1942–45; Dr. George H. A. Clowes, vice president, 1937–38, president, 1938–39; Dr. Jacob Furth, president, 1957–58; Dr. Theodore S. Hauschka, vice president, 1958–59, president, 1959–60; Dr. James Holland, president, 1970–71; and Dr. Enrico Mihich, president, 1987–88.

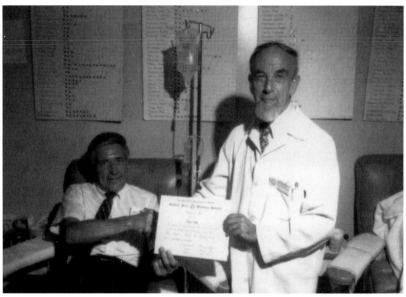

**6-51.**
Dr. Elias Cohen with donor in Plasmapheresis Donor Center.

The Institute also made an interesting contribution to the history of the AACR. When the AACR decided to publish its organizational history, many of the early records were missing. Some of the records were thought to have been entrusted to Dr. Alphonse Thibaudeau, chief of Pathology at Roswell Park and an early AACR officer from 1936 to 1945. Mrs. Isabelle Herger, Dr. Thibaudeau's daughter and a histology technician in Dr. Mirand's laboratory at the Institute, accidentally found records of the AACR from 1907 through 1940 in the attic of the family homestead. This *find* was largely responsible for the publication of the AACR history to be published in the February 1961 issue of the Cancer Research journal.

Dr. Moore's administration not only contributed significantly to the clinical and scientific parts of the mission of the Institute, but the educational component as well. Dr. Moore felt that as a comprehensive cancer center, the Institute must emphasize not only accumulating medical and scientific knowledge within its walls, but sharing that knowledge with colleagues and the public through an ambitious educational program.

For example, relations between Roswell Park and the University of Buffalo and its Medical School improved rapidly during Dr. Moore's administration. The independence of the Institute and the quality of its new staff were recognized by the University. Dr. John Payne, professor of Surgery, Dr. Henry M. Woodburn, dean of the Graduate School and professor of Chemistry, and President Clifford Furnas were especially helpful in developing conjoined programs and helping to establish the Roswell Park Graduate Division in 1955. The fact that President Furnas was appointed to the Institute's Board of Visitors helped solidify educational relations. Further evidence of the close relationship was the appointment of Dr. Moore to the Graduate School Committee, the Nuclear Center, and subsequently his receipt of the Chancellor's Medal. All helped forge this close relationship.

The Roswell Park Graduate Division was under the direction of Dr. Edwin A. Mirand until December 18, 1997, when he was succeeded by his able assistant Dr. Arthur M. Michalek. Students can complete graduate research programs leading to master's and doctoral degrees in ten scientific disciplines with an emphasis on cancer. The Graduate Division has graduated over 1,400 students from all over the world since 1955.

Dr. Moore also initiated a post-doctoral program in basic and clinical fields. At that time, Roswell Park had many foreign basic science postdoctoral students, residents, and fellows. A large contingent from Japan followed the single appointment of a surgical resident named Dr. T. T. Kondo in 1955. In one city in Japan, there were five professors of surgery who had trained at Roswell Park and one who had served as president of the Japanese Surgical Society.

**6-52.**
Dr. Clifford Furnas in 1964. Chancellor and then President of the University of Buffalo, he was a member of our Board of Visitors. Dr. Moore and he had a superb relationship which benefited our relationship with the University.

In 1953 Dr. Moore encouraged Dr. Mirand to develop the Research Participation Program in Science (RPPS) with support of the New York State Department of Health and the National Science Foundation (NSF). This program is held each summer for medical, dental, college, and high school students to encourage young men and women to adopt scientific careers and to exercise creativity in the study of cancer problems. This program was adopted by the NSF in 1958, after Sputnik had demonstrated the importance of providing science early in the educational careers of students. The NSF invited Dr. Mirand to assist in developing a national program. The scope and importance of the program has grown steadily for forty-six consecutive summers under Dr. Mirand's supervision, with additional support from the National Cancer Institute. Many of the over 8,000 graduates of this program have successfully pursued careers in science. The staff cooperated immensely to make the RPPS a success.

**6-53.**
Dr. Moore and Dr. Dorita
Norton lecturing to
summer students. Dr.
Moore enjoyed and
urged the presence of
students on campus.

**6-54.**
Dr. Gabor Markus (right)
with a student.

At this time, also, the Department of Nursing Education, headed by Assistant Director of Nursing Miss Patricia E. Burns, was recognized formally as a Division of the University's School of Nursing. Qualified members of the Department of Nursing, who were carrying major responsibilities for educational programs, were given appropriate status on the faculty of Nursing.

Another of Dr. Moore's contributions was made in 1955, when he proposed the formation of the Association of Cancer Institute Directors (ACID) and invited R. Lee Clark, the director of M.D. Anderson, Houston, Texas, to join him in this enterprise. The first few meetings of ACID were held at Roswell Park. The Association continues today as the Association of American Cancer Institutes. Dr. Mirand has been secretary-treasurer of this Association from 1967 to the present time.

The Roswell Park Surgical Society was established in memory of Dr. Roswell Park in 1954. This organization, which currently has more than 200 members, consists of surgical residents, regular surgical staff, and other professional persons associated with surgery in the community.

In the summer of 1967, Dr. George E. Moore was appointed State Director of Public Health Research, requiring his time at both Buffalo and Albany. He retired from New York State service March 14, 1973, and left for Denver, Colorado, where he continued his surgery and research at hospitals and at the medical school in Denver. The Board of Visitors of Roswell Park on March 9, 1973, in a citation, recognized his great contributions to the Institute: *The Board of Visitors hereby acknowledges the manifold contributions of George E. Moore, Jr., to the development of Roswell Park Memorial Institute in his capacity as Institute director from 1952 to 1967. Without his dedication in attracting prominent physicians and scientists to the staff, initiating innovative cancer programs and expanding the physical plant, the Institute would not have attained the significant position it holds in the national and international scene.*

**6-55.**
Nancy Burke, staff nurse
orienting Niagara
University student nurse.

**6-56.**
Collection of head
nurses carrying out
major responsibilities
for clinical and
educational programs.

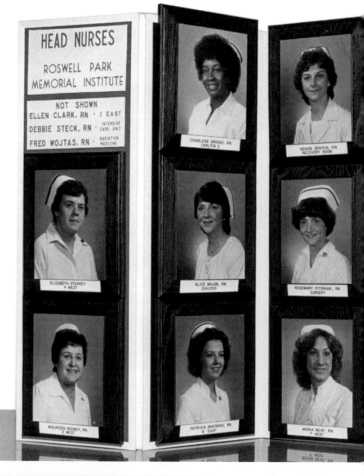

**6-57.**
Staff nurses in front
of Seventy-fifth
Anniversary mural in
Research Studies Center
registering students. Back
row, from left to right: D.
Wonch, E. Zupa. Front
row: K. Ginn, C. Lyons,
and B. Slusarski.

**6-58.**
Mrs. Anna Aungst,
the head nurse, whom
trainees and staff enjoyed.

**6-59.**
Dr. and Mrs. G. Moore
off to Albany with Insti-
tute plane. Dr. Moore's
busy schedule required
flying at his convenience
from Buffalo to Albany,
particularly as State
director of Public Health
Research. Both had
licenses to fly. Mrs.
Moore devoted a great
deal of her time to
Institute activities.

**7-1.**
Dr. James T. Grace, Jr.,
lecturing to Institute
staff members.

······························································1970········

**7-2.**
Dr. Grace with
Dr. S. Iwakata
(standing) in Viral
Oncology Laboratory.

Dr. James T. Grace, Jr., assistant director at Roswell Park since 1959, became the sixth Institute director in the summer of 1967, following Dr. Moore's appointment as New York State director of Public Health Research stationed in Albany and in Buffalo at Roswell Park. Dr. Grace was a graduate of Yale University and Harvard Medical School. In addition to his administrative duties, Dr. Grace continued to carry out clinical studies in gastrointestinal surgery and extensive research concerning the role of viruses in tumor formation. Dr. Grace and his colleagues were well recognized at that time for their contributions to viral carcinogenesis.

The Institute was becoming so diversified that Dr. Grace, who wanted to keep a proper balance between research, treatment, and education, appointed associate Institute directors to assist in running specific areas of the Institute in 1967. Dr. William H. Wehr was named associate Institute director for Clinical Affairs. Dr. David Pressman, Bronfman Award winner and head of the Department of Biochemistry, was named associate Institute director for Scientific Affairs. Dr. Edwin A. Mirand, head of the West Seneca Laboratories and director of the Institute's education programs, was appointed associate Institute director for Educational Affairs. Dr. Mirand headed the Department of Education that was officially formed during the administration of Dr. Moore on April 2, 1965, from 1967 to December 18, 1997.

**7-3.**
Dr. Norman Schaaf
(right) with resident
in Regional Center for
Maxillofacial Prosthetics.

What had been two separate Head and Neck Surgery departments under Dr. Frank Marchetta and Dr. F. W. Hoffmeister were reorganized and consolidated under the direction of Dr. Donald P. Shedd in 1967. That same year, significant advances were made in the surgical and non-surgical reconstruction of patients with defects in the head and neck areas after surgery to remove their cancers. Dr. Vahram Bakamjian developed the deltopectoral flap for surgical reconstruction. The *Bakamjian Flap* is still used worldwide and is still considered the state-of-the-art in reconstructive surgery.

Roswell Park became the site of the Regional Center for Maxillofacial Prosthetics, under Dr. Norman G. Schaaf, one of only a dozen such centers in the United States. Prostheses, artificial devices used to replace missing parts of the body, are custom-designed to help rehabilitate cancer and trauma patients who have head and neck defects or injuries.

In 1968 two staff members left the Institute after long service with great loyalty, skill, and dedication. Dr. Harold A. Solomon, chief of the Department of Dental Surgery, and Dr. William H. Wehr, associate Institute director for Clinical Affairs, and former acting director, both of whom had joined the Institute staff in 1931, retired. Dr. Norman G. Schaaf replaced Dr. Solomon and the department was renamed the Department of Dentistry and Maxillofacial Prosthetics. Dr. Wehr's duties were assumed by Dr. Gerald P. Murphy, who came to Roswell Park in 1968 to continue collaborations in erythropoietin research with Dr. Mirand, as the chief of the Urology Department, replacing Dr. Marvin Woodruff, and as director of the Department of Experimental Surgery.

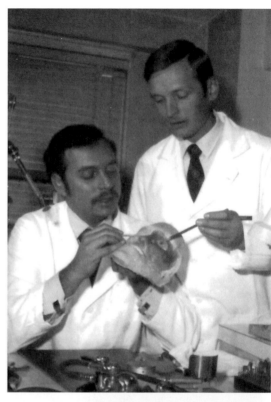

**7-4.**
Dr. Richard Steeves
working on rat in Viral
Oncology Laboratory of
Drs. Grace and Mirand.

90

**7-5.**
Dr. Grace with Dr.
Mittelman (right) and
Dr. Ralph Jones (left)
re-opening the Clinical
Research Facility on
2-West in the Hospital
Building.

The hallmark of Dr. Grace's administration was also research, both laboratory and clinical. The staff, including Dr. Grace himself, pursued new avenues of research and refined existing concepts in an attempt to advance the search for the causes of and treatments for cancer. Research highlights are chronicled in the following paragraphs.

Dr. David Pressman's research program at that time focused on the applications of antibodies in the study of neoplastic diseases and in the basic studies of the structure of proteins and the nature of biological receptor sites. His research team of Dr. Christopher Carruthers, Dr. Eugene Day, Dr. Alan Grossberg, Dr. Oliver Roholt, Dr. Yasuo Yagi, Dr. Ben Seon and others, was deeply involved with the use of fluorescent and radioactive labeled antibodies with the goal of developing antibodies which could carry enough radioactivity to a tumor to accomplish therapy or a specific diagnostic test. The physical and chemical nature of the antibody molecule itself and the nature of its reaction with its antigen were also being studied to provide information on protein structure and the nature of biological combining sites.

Dr. David Harker, with Dr. Dorita Norton, Dr. Harold Box, Dr. G. Kartha, Dr. Jake Bello, Dr. R. R. Parthasarathy, and others, was conducting x-crystallographic studies which led to the determination of the crystal and molecular structure of twenty-two biologically important substances and, using three-dimensional models based on electron density, construction of maps of the ribonuclease molecule.

Dr. Michael Laskowski, Dr. Eugene Sulkowski, and Dr. Lawrence Kress were studying DNAses and their use in studies of the primary structure of nucleic acids and basic trypsin inhibitors of the pancreas.

**7-6.**
Dr. Grace with head
nurse showing Lawrence
Welk (right) through
Clinical Research Facility
on 2-West.

**7-8.**
Betty Basty, a nurse
working in a patient
germ free environment.

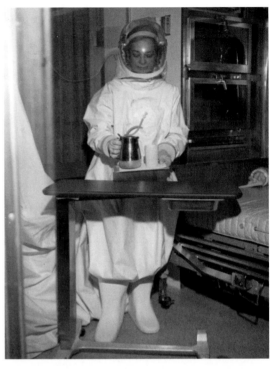

Drs. Edwin Mirand and Dr. Gerald P. Murphy
were studying growth control by endocrine mechanisms; erythropoietin production in kidney grafts
as an effective source of erythropoietin; anephric
patients showing an extrarenal source of erythropoietin; and, with Dr. James T. Grace, Jr., erythro-
poiesis stimulated by polycythemia-induced virus.

Other research projects during Dr. Grace's admin-
istrations included: Dr. Theodore Hauschka and
Barbara Holdridge, histocompatibility antigens;
Dr. S. G. Cudkowicz and Michael Bennett, prog-
enitor cells in marrow and spleen; Drs. Donald
Metcalf and R. Foster, behavior on transfer of
serum-stimulated bone marrow colonies; Dr.
Leonard Weiss and staff, the physicochemical
nature of the cell periphery in determining the
metastatic behavior of cancer cells; and Drs.
Charles Nichol, Enrico Mihich, Maire T. Hakala,
S. F. Zakrzewski, A. Bloch, W. C. Werkheiser, G.
Tritsch and others, new compounds that may
antagonize vitamin functions or interfere with the
biosynthesis of nucleic acids and proteins.

Also, Drs. James Holland, J. S. Bekesi, G. Costa,
O. S. Selawry, and others, were studying intensifi-
cation of chemotherapy and more effective supportive treatment using platelet transfusions and
*germ free* status. Drs. E. Carter, R. R. Ellison,
and Jerome W. Yates were evaluating adriamycin
in the treatment of acute myelogenous leukemia in
adults. Dr. Joseph Sokal and staff were developing
chemotherapy protocols for lymphomas and
leukemias using combination chemotherapy. Dr.
Avery A. Sandberg was investigating viruses and
chromosome damage and the role of chromosomes
in causing cancer and leukemias. Dr. Merrill A.
Bender and Dr. Monte Blau were continuing their
work to develop a general radioactive tumor local-
izing agent that would permit the early detection
of many neoplasms by radioisotope scanning
techniques. Drs. Grace, David Yohn, Julius
Horozewicz, Rita Buffett, Robert Zeigel, James
Blakalee, Y. Hinuma, Susan Leong, R. Steeves, W.
H. Munyon, Edwin A. Mirand, and others, were
studying the possible role of viruses in the etiology
of human malignant disease. Dr. Gerald P. Murphy
established a four-bed Chronic Hemodialysis Unit
in the Department of Urology.

**7-9.**
Dr. Grace presenting a certificate to Professor C. Cori at the time of first Cori Lecture. Left to right: Mrs. George, Moore, Prof. Cori and his wife, Dr. J. Grace, and Mrs. Betty Grace.

**7-10.**
WATS (Wide Area Telephone Service) advertisement.

As a cancer patient referral facility, physicians at Roswell Park worked closely with referring physicians. To facilitate this process and to encourage more referrals, a WATS (Wide Area Telephone Service) system was installed in 1968. The WATS line made it possible for over 50,000 physicians, dentists, and osteopaths in New York State to telephone Institute staff members, toll-free, twenty-four-hours-a-day, to refer patients to the Institute, discuss patients they had referred to the Institute, and to obtain assistance in treating their cancer patients. During its first year of operation, over 2,300 calls were received by Institute physicians.

To honor Drs. Carl and Gerty Cori, the first Cori Lecture was presented at the Institute.

On March 8, 1970, tragedy struck the Roswell Park family when Dr. James T. Grace, Jr., was critically injured in an automobile accident that claimed the life of his wife after co-hosting a reception at a staff member's residence in South Wales, New York, for academic administrators of local academic institutions. After initial treatment locally at Buffalo General Hospital, Dr. Grace was transferred to the Veterans Administration Hospital in Newington, Connecticut, under the excellent care of our former chief of Neurosurgery, Dr. Guy Owens, where he died August 13, 1971.

**7-11.**
Dr. Grace's often quoted position on cancer research. Students reviewing bronze plaque quotation located in Outpatient Building.

**8-1.**
Dr. Gerald P. Murphy talking to former Senate Majority Leader, later Judge, Walter Mahoney, who became an aggressive supporter of the Institute like Assemblyman Gugino. The Simpson, Kress, Moore, Grace, and Murphy administrations benefited from his dependable support.

# Chapter 8

# Surge Ahead and Respond to Challenges: The Murphy Years

**8-2.**
Dr. Murphy with Dr. P. Greco (brother of Assemblyman Steve Greco), Mr. P. Rubino, Mr. Elmer Lux, and Former Assemblyman F. Gugino. Mr. F. Gugino was an aggressive supporter of the Institute as chairman of the Cancer Survey Commission that helped us get the Simpson Building in Simpson administration and the postwar project in expanding the hospital in the Kress administration. Mr. Elmer Lux was the Institute's able contact, along with Assembly S. Greco, with the Governor's Office, particularly with Governor Malcolm Wilson.

Dr. Gerald P. Murphy, who had been acting Institute director since Dr. Grace's accident, became the seventh Institute director November 11, 1970. Dr. Murphy can be remembered, like Dr. Moore, as a very active director, contributing greatly to the expansion of research programs and facilities, ensuring that the Institute and its mission were well represented in state, national, international cancer communities, and to the Board of Visitors. He urged his staff to assume responsibility to do likewise.

Dr. Murphy earned his M.D. at the University of Washington in Seattle, interned at the Johns Hopkins Hospital in Baltimore, and served a residency at the Brady Urological Institute at Johns Hopkins. Before coming to Roswell Park, Dr. Murphy was research associate and chief in the Department of Surgical Physiology at the Walter Reed Army Institute of Research in Washington, D.C., and assistant professor of Urology at Johns Hopkins Medical School. He also participated in urological and transplantation research on the Faculty of Medicine of the University of Stellenbosch, Capetown Province, South Africa.

**8-3.**
Dr. Murphy meets with the Board of Visitors in 1972. In the back row are, from left to right: Dr. D. Pressman, Dr. E. Mirand, Mr. M. Rodzenko, Mr. R. Goehle, and Dr. Charles Eckhert. Front row: Mr. A. Kirchhofer, Dr. Kenneth Goldman, Dr. Curtis Lind, and Dr. John Ambrusko, members of the Board of Visitors.

**8-4.**
The Board of Visitors in 1977 meeting in Butler Hall at Butler Mansion. Left to right: Mr. Peter J. Crotty, Sr., Mr. Alfred Kirchhofer, Dr. Gerald P. Murphy, Dr. Charles F. Elliot, Dr. Robert Ketter, and Dr. Edward D. Coates (NYS Health Department). Mr. P. Crotty, like Mr. A. Kirchhofer, was a great supporter of the Institute. Dr. R. Ketter, President of SUNY/Buffalo, always assisted us in developing effective relationships with the University.

**8-5.**
Dr. Murphy pays a
visit to President Ronald
Reagan. With him is
Amanda Blake, popular
TV actress.

**8-7.**
Governor Hugh L. Carey
with Mr. Peter J. Crotty,
Sr., and Dr. G. P. Murphy
touring Hospital facilities.

**8-6.**
First Lady, Mrs. Rosalind
Carter, with Dr. Mirand in
Buffalo. She signed the
Guest Book at that time.

Soon after coming to Roswell Park as a result of
Dr. Mirand's sponsorship, Dr. Murphy established
in 1967 a program of research involving kidney
transplantation, and expanded the Institute's
Hemodialysis Unit for the treatment of cancer
patients with kidney disease. The nursing staff
which assisted Dr. Murphy on this unit included
Kathleen Robie, Alice Major, D. Walker, and J.
Liu. He also resumed collaborative studies on
erythropoietin with Dr. Mirand, which they had
begun while Dr. Murphy was in South Africa
at the University of Stellenbosch and at Johns
Hopkins University. Like Dr. Moore, Dr. Murphy
surged ahead on all fronts to improve facilities
and programs by nurturing good relationships
with the Governor, the Governor's office, New
York State legislators, the New York State
Department of Health and cancer constituencies
nationally and internationally.

**8-8.**
Research Studies Center.

**8-9.**
Cancer Drug Center.

The New York State legislature appropriated $3,407,716 in 1970 to begin construction of the Research Studies Center to house conference rooms and classrooms, administrative divisions and departments, the Education Office, a 650-seat auditorium, the Computer Center and the Medical & Scientific Library which has over 89,000 volumes of journals, serials, monographs, and audiovisual materials on oncology and related disciplines.

Also in 1971 construction of the Cancer Drug Center began at the corner of Carlton and Elm Streets. The total cost was $4,255,806, including $2,205,130 in New York State funds, $1,315,000 in federal funds, and $735,676 in private contributions. Private contributors to the Cancer Drug Center Fund included not only organizations such as the Baird Foundation, the Buffalo Foundation, the James H. Cummings Foundation, the Julia R. and Estelle L. Foundation, the Twin Coach Charitable Foundation, Inc., and the Western New York Foundation, but individuals, such as Mr. Harvey Gaylord, son of the second director of the Institute.

Cornerstones for the Cancer Drug Center and the Research Studies Center were laid on September 24, 1971. Officials from Buffalo, Erie County, and New York State spoke at the ceremonies. Speaking for Governor Nelson A. Rockefeller, who was unable to attend, State Health Commissioner Dr. Hollis S. Ingraham said that the Governor *takes great pride and pleasure in these imposing new buildings, which are evidence of the dramatic leadership the administration has provided in efforts to improve the health and well-being of the citizens of this state.* In a letter submitted for the occasion, Dr. Leonell C. Strong, former director of the Biological Station at Springville, expressed the opinion that *an appreciation of the genetic import will be the ultimate key to the solution of the cancer problem, including its cure.*

Cornerstone festivities for Cancer Drug Center. Left to right: County Executive John Tutuska, Mayor Frank Sedita of Buffalo, NYS Commissioner of Health Dr. Hollis Ingraham, Dr. Enrico Mihich, Dr. Murphy, and Reverend Kenneth Slattery, President of Niagara University.

Dr. Gerald P. Murphy and Dr. James T. Grace, Jr., had worked very hard to obtain approval and funds for construction of the Cancer Drug Center. Under the circumstances, the Board of Visitors recommended to Governor Rockefeller that the building be designated the James T. Grace, Jr., Cancer Drug Center. In a letter dated January 21, 1972, to Health Commissioner Ingraham, the Governor stated, *I am happy to endorse your proposal to rename the Cancer Drug Center Building at Roswell Park Memorial Institute the "James T. Grace, Jr., Cancer Drug Center Building," in honor of the late Doctor Grace.* Commissioner Hollis S. Ingraham represented Governor Rockefeller on May 8, 1972, to commemorate the renaming of the Cancer Drug Center. Dr. Ingraham said, *Three quarters of a century ago, the State of New York planted a seed here, when it gave Dr. Roswell Park a grant of $10,000 to seek the causes of cancer. It was also the beginning of New York State's commitment to medical research in general, a commitment that has repeatedly demonstrated its worth as State Health Department scientists have opened new doors to knowledge.*

The James T. Grace, Jr., Cancer Drug Center, one of the first buildings in the world to provide for an essentially complete preclinical program of anticancer drug development and testing under one roof, opened in 1973. The Experimental Therapeutics Department is housed in this Center.

**8-11.**

Kevin Guest House at 782 Ellicott Street provides patients and loved ones of patients at RPCI warmth, understanding, and a homelike atmosphere. It took Rev. Edward Ulaszeski (Father Ed), Francis Sturner, and an attorney from Sharon, Pennsylvania, Cyril Garvey, to acquire and renovate the three-story frame house in order to establish Kevin Guest House with the assistance of Miss Virginia Brady, director of Social Services at RPCI.

Most patients hospitalized at Roswell Park are brought to the Institute by members of their families. Often relatives want to stay near the Institute while patients are being treated, especially if they are very far from Buffalo. Many relatives stay in local motels and hotels, but many cannot afford these accommodations. Dr. Murphy's discussions with Mr. Cyril T. Garvey, of the Garvey Foundation, resulted in the purchasing of a house one block from the Institute in 1972 to provide low-cost housing for patients and their families. A group of local volunteers remodeled the house and it was named the Kevin Guest House, in honor of Mr. Garvey's son, Kevin, who had died of cancer at Roswell Park. The Kevin Guest House is the oldest hospitality house in the United States and was the prototype for the Ronald McDonald Houses. The Kevin Guest House Corporation, which owned and operated the Kevin Guest House, acquired additional dwellings near the original house, renovated them and developed the Kevin Guest House Complex to serve Roswell Park patients.

Because new and more effective forms of treatment are constantly being developed, departments such as Radiation Medicine continually update the weapons in their arsenal against cancer. In 1973, an $800,000 35 Me V linear accelerator was purchased which uses high energy radiation to treat cancer by x-rays or electrons.

As long as cancer exists, so will the need for many types of research activities, which carry out clinical, experimental, and educational functions. On June 29, 1972, the Institute, through Dr. Murphy's efforts in submitting a Construction Grant to the National Cancer Institute, received its largest federal grant in its seventy-seven-year history to build the Cancer Cell Center in the block bounded by Ellicott, Carlton, Oak, and Elm Streets. The Cancer Cell Center permitted more intensive study of the cancer cell and its interactions by the departments of Molecular Immunology, Experimental Pathology, and Molecular Medicine than was possible in the Institute's other facilities. The total cost of the facility was $7.83 million which was comprised of a $5.497 million grant from the National Cancer Institute and $2.333 million provided by New York State. Governor Malcolm Wilson laid the cornerstone for the Cancer Cell Center in 1974.

**8-12.**
Governor Malcolm Wilson with Commissioner of Health Dr. Hollis Ingraham and Dr. Murphy at the occasion of laying the cornerstone of Cancer Cell Center in 1974.

**8-13.**
Cancer Cell Center.

In response to the increased demand for clinical research and treatment facilities and to meet the demand for future growth, it became imperative that the hospital expand its existing bed capacity and upgrade outpatient facilities. In August 1974 the State of New York was able to purchase the 258-bed Carlton House Nursing Home at the corner of Carlton and Oak Streets and all of its contents for $5 million. This addition increased the bed capacity to 525, thereby enabling Roswell Park to take advantage of additional treatment, research and educational funds available, particularly from federal sources. As part of a subsequent remodeling program, a glass-enclosed, overhead walkway was constructed to connect the Carlton House to the main hospital.

To replace the four-bed Intensive Care Unit opened in 1969, a ten-bed Intensive Care Unit opened April 8, 1974, under the supervision of Dr. Raymond J. Trudnowski, chief of Anesthesiology, with the assistance of Sue Lippert, Janice Lisboa, and Noma Roberson.

With longer periods of remission and greater control of various forms of cancer, the concept of rehabilitating the cancer patient became a priority. In 1974, with this concept in mind, the Cancer Patient Rehabilitation Center, which incorporated twelve clinical and social services, was dedicated in memory of R. James Christie, a former patient and dedicated worker as an American Cancer Society volunteer in the field of laryngectomee rehabilitation.

With the expansion of the hospital completed, attention turned to the outpatient facilities. When ground was broken for the $3.7 million Ambulatory Services Building, Governor Hugh L. Carey dedicated the Ambulatory Services building on July 30, 1975, and the building was opened officially in October 1976. At the dedication, Governor Carey noted that, *there will be no longer inadequate space or lack of privacy to care for the patients and the outpatient clinics will be serviced more effectively and efficiently by the staff.* The Ambulatory Services Building included the new Main Entrance and spacious outpatient clinics for Medical Oncology, Breast Surgery, General Surgery and associated services, Gynecologic Oncology, Dermatology and Chemosurgery, Pediatrics and Neurosurgery Departments.

**8-14.**
Ambulatory Services
Building under
construction.

Parking had been a persistent problem at the
Institute, and hospital expansion and new
outpatient facilities only added to the problem.
To ease the parking shortage for staff and
patients, a three-tier, protected Parking Ramp
was completed at a cost of $2.6 million, in the
block bounded by Carlton, Elm, and Virginia
Streets and Michigan Avenue.

The Butler Mansion at the corner of Delaware
Avenue and North Street was purchased for
Roswell Park's use with a grant of $105,000 from
the Baird Foundation obtained by Dr. Mirand, for
activities of the Volunteers of Roswell Park, Inc.,
and the Society to Aid Roswell (STAR). The
Kevin Guest House, Inc., aided Dr. Mirand in purchasing the property. The mansion is one of the
few examples of Stanford White Architecture in
the Buffalo area. It was the home of Mr. Edward
H. Butler, Sr., who helped Dr. Park establish the
Institute. Later, Edward H. Butler, Jr., lived in the
mansion with his wife Kate R. Butler, who died
August 3, 1974. Roswell Park called it Butler Hall
and used the facility as a meeting place for volunteer groups, patient entertainment programs and
public and professional education programs and
conferences. Butler Mansion was sold to Sports
Systems for $500,000 several years later because
of staff disinterest in using the facility.

**8-16.**
Like Dr. G. Moore,
Dr. G. P. Murphy
recognized the
importance of keeping
friends and active
contacts with the
"Trinity" (Governor's
Office, NYS
Commissioner of
Health's Office, and
State legislators). On
July 20, 1975, Governor
Hugh L. Carey dedicated
the Ambulatory Services
Building and took time
out to sign the Guest
Book. Dr. Murphy is
showing him some of
the past outstanding and
historical signatures.

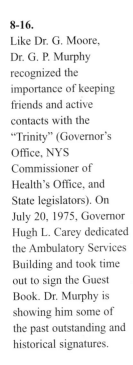

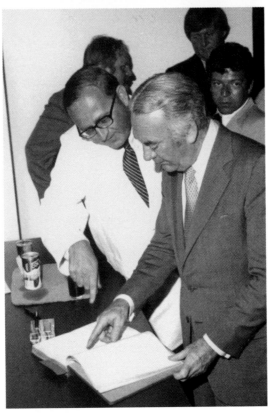

Late in 1975 Roswell Park acquired the stately Butler Mansion at Delaware and North Street with the aid of contributions from the Baird Foundation who responded to grant request from Dr. Mirand totaling $105,000, the amount to purchase the property from Mrs. Kate Butler Wallis. Dr. Mirand is grateful to Mrs. Theodore VanAntwerp to interest Mr. Baird, her former husband, to respond to Dr. Mirand's request and her cousin Mrs. Kate Butler Wallis to sell the property to RPCI.

The mansion, one of the few examples in the Buffalo area of the famous turn-of-the-century architect Stanford White, was the home of Mrs. Kate R. Butler, who had died on August 3, 1974. She was the widow of Edward H. Butler, Jr., whose father had founded the BUFFALO EVENING NEWS and was the chief supporter of Dr. Park in founding the Institute in 1898.

Known as Butler Hall, it served as a meeting place for volunteer groups and as a site for concerts and other entertainment programs for patients as well as public and professional meetings for cancer education lectures. It was later sold to Sports Services for $500,000, since RPCI staff lacked interest to sustain it.

Before Dr. Lucius Sinks left for the National Cancer Institute, he had begun work on establishing an Adolescent Unit to meet the special social, emotional, and treatment needs of teenage cancer patients. The first such unit in the United States opened January 5, 1978. The creation of this unique unit was made possible by a $337,685 grant from the National Cancer Institute, a $25,000 contribution from the National Football League which Congressman Jack Kemp helped secure, a $4,000 donation from the Society to Aid Roswell (STAR), and contributions from Mr. Ralph Wilson, owner of the Buffalo Bills.

The Kirchhofer Conference Room on the fourth floor of the Main Building was dedicated to Mr. Alfred H. Kirchhofer, then in his thirty-fifth year as a member of the Board of Visitors. The patient and visitor waiting area in the Department of Radiation Medicine was named in honor of Dr. Walter T. Murphy, one of the early chiefs of Radiation Medicine.

A Cancer Prevention-Detection Center was established to identify individuals at high risk of developing cancer. The comprehensive examination was provided to thousands of individuals at no charge.

**8-19.**
Buffalo Bills' owner, Mr. Ralph Wilson, visited the Institute with Dr. Murphy. Mr. Wilson at that time contributed to the new Adolescent Unit at the Institute. He was a former patient and was grateful for the effective treatment he received.

A Cancer Research Containment Facility was designed in Dr. Moore's Cell Plant adjacent to the Cell and Virus Building. This renovated facility provided a research laboratory with specific safeguards to minimize exposure to hazardous biological and chemical materials. The first floor was renovated to provide laboratory space for the expanded interferon research program. The second floor was designed for recombinant DNA, cloning of mouse and viral genes, radioiodination studies, and environmental carcinogen studies.

Although Roswell Park's campus had expanded significantly in the 1970s, by 1984 it was apparent that major renovations to the hospital were needed. Governor Mario Cuomo responded by proposing that the State budget not only increase the Institute's operating budget by $4 million over the previous year to $60.5 million, but allocate an additional $580,000 in capital construction funds for the hospital, of which $150,000 would be earmarked to hire a consultant to assess and rank the facility's capital needs.

The William H. Wehr Research Center was dedicated January 18, 1980, culminating a $1.9 million project that centralized research programs involving chemical carcinogens and immunodeprived mice in a facility with adequate biohazard containment safeguards.

What would become one of the most controversial and most challenging issues in the history of Roswell Park began to evolve in 1984, when Commissioner of Health Dr. David Axelrod initially spoke to Dr. Edwin A. Mirand about considering plans to study the feasibility of moving Roswell Park inpatients to space leased in the newly built, neighboring Buffalo General Hospital. The rationale for considering the plan was that Roswell Park's thirty-year-old hospital building (known as Building 7) was *out of date and inefficient compared with modern standards* and would require $8.2 million in repairs and cost $125 million to replace. Dr. Axelrod's proposal stated that Roswell Park would remain a *discrete, independent institution* at Buffalo General Hospital.

When Dr. Murphy was informed by Dr. Mirand of the Commissioner's conversation, he commissioned an independent study in response to Dr. Axelrod's proposal. The blue-ribbon panel of cancer experts (Dr. R. Lee Clark, founder and director of M.D. Anderson; Dr. William Hutchinson, founder and first director of Fred Hutchinson Cancer Center; Dr. Frank Rauscher, past director of the National Cancer Institute; and Dr. C. Chester Stock, past vice president of Memorial Sloan-Kettering), convened by the Roswell Park administration, concluded that the transfer of Institute beds and other services to Buffalo General Hospital *would abrogate the years of foresight, dreams, and efforts embodied in the Institute and would diminish its role as a comprehensive cancer center. We speak to the survival of the Institute. The cumulative effect of relocation of inpatient facilities outside the cancer center would include the demise of traditional patterns of referral and compromise the conduct of clinical trials, the development of basic research, the quality of patient care, commitments to training, and the nature of the staff attracted to the Institute. In short, this single act will terminate the ability of Roswell Park Memorial (now Cancer) Institute to maintain a comprehensive cancer research, treatment, and education program.* A groundswell of support to block the move, particularly from Dr. Murphy, the staff, the public, and legislators, developed quickly. The 1,165-member Erie County Medical Society called the proposed plan a *profound disaster.*

In a May 15, 1984, letter to the BUFFALO NEWS, Health Commissioner Dr. David Axelrod had to back down from his original proposal and pledged that he would be *party to no proposal or plan which could compromise Roswell Park Memorial Institute's integrity or negatively impact on patient care and research.* Dr. Axelrod said clinical facilities must be replaced or renovated if the State was to *protect and enhance the Institute's reputation, position and ability to provide the highest quality patient care and leading role in cancer research.*

In the meantime, the New York State Department of Health continued to review its position on how to proceed with Roswell Park's needs. In October 1984 the Department of Health released a lengthy report which called the relocation of Roswell Park's inpatient beds *technically feasible,* but stopped short of recommending or endorsing such a move.

Commissioner of Health Axelrod re-emphasized the State's *continuous commitment* to Roswell Park and indicated that the transfer of inpatient beds to Buffalo General Hospital was no longer an option. The Institute had won the fight to remain at one site—a comprehensive cancer center—thanks to the successful and courageous efforts of Dr. Murphy and the staff in mobilizing the opposition to such a proposal.

A number of programs took shape during the Murphy administration, including those highlighted in the following paragraphs.

Dr. Holland started a Germfree Unit which was supervised by members of the nursing staff, particularly Ms. Doris Burnett and Ms. Audrey Tuttolomondo. This new, four-bed unit, and prototype for other germfree units in the country, started in 1963 as a research project with one Life Island Unit. The basis for this Unit was established from basic research done at the Institute by Dr. Mirand and Dr. Patricia Bealmear. Patients being treated with chemotherapy were kept in this Unit until their bodies were strong enough to protect themselves against infections.

**8-21.**
Joyce Jividen conducting an experiment in germfree plastic isolator.

Public education had been a priority at the Institute since the early 1940s under Dr. Kress. However, in September 1973, Dr. Mirand took public education to a new level when he started the CAN-DIAL system. CAN-DIAL is a telephone access, public cancer information system that enables individuals to call Roswell Park and listen to tape-recorded messages on a variety of cancer topics. During the first year, 45,000 calls were received from Buffalo and Erie County. In 1974 CAN-DIAL was expanded to cover New York State, and Spanish language tapes were added. The CAN-DIAL program has been the model for similar programs nationally and internationally, and formed the concept on which the National Cancer Institute based the creation of its Cancer Information Service network in 1976.

By 1979 epidemiological studies at the Institute had identified that daughters of mothers who had taken diethylstibesterol (DES) during pregnancy were at greater risk of developing cervical cancer than the general population. Studies also found that adults whose acne was treated with radiation in their teens were at greater risk than the general population for developing thyroid cancer. Roswell Park established the DES Screening Clinic, within the Department of Gynecologic Oncology, and the Thyroid Screening Clinic, within the Department of Medical Oncology, to monitor these groups.

Molecular/cellular biology and genetics had become two of the more prominent scientific disciplines in the field of cancer research. Roswell Park recognized these new directions in research and in 1980 organized the Department of Cell & Tumor Biology under the direction of Dr. Darrell J. Doyle, and the Department of Human Genetics, which included a Genetics Counseling Service, under the direction of Dr. Thomas B. Shows.

**8-22.**
Cancer Information Service, in the early days of the operation, supervised by Mr. Russell Sciandra, with staff members Diane Ruesch and Ramon Melendez.

**8-23.**
Staff and graduate students of the Cell & Tumor Biology Department.

**8-24.**

Dr. Michael Zevon
with his staff in
first Department
of Psychology at
the Institute.

At the same time, the Institute was expanding its patient care services and creating new educational opportunities. The Intitute's first Department of Psychology was established under the direction of clinical psychologist Dr. Michael A. Zevon to provide counseling and psychological support to nearly 400 cancer patients and their families each year. For the first time, Roswell Park offered internships to clinical psychologists through formal educational programs. The Patient Transport Service, an expanded version of the former Patient Escort Service, also was established. Roswell Park and the Visiting Nursing Association agreed to offer liaison nursing through the Institute's outpatient services.

Roswell Park established the John W. Pickren Lecture to honor the memory of Dr. John Pickren, a nationally recognized authority on cancer pathology. Dr. Pickren had been the chief of the Department of Pathology from 1955 until his death in 1984.

Roswell Park established a *Stop Smoking Hotline* within the Cancer Information Service. To provide an important resource for the general public and patients, New York State Health Commissioner Dr. David Axelrod announced the establishment of a statewide toll-free AIDS hotline at Roswell Park. The hotline was funded to Dr. Mirand through the State's 1983 AIDS appropriation, which allocated $4 million for AIDS research, $600,000 for community education and outreach programs, and $150,000 for public information.

On February 11, 1985, Dr. Gerald P. Murphy and New York State Attorney General Robert Abrams called on the New York State legislature to pass a bill requiring that smokeless tobacco products and advertising carry a warning that these products were addictive and caused cancer. The bill was part of a concerted effort to include warnings about the danger of smokeless tobacco products similar to those appearing on cigarette packaging and advertising.

The Greater Buffalo Area Black Nurse Association held its first informational/membership meeting June 30, 1985. Roswell Park nurses Verdis Griffin, RN, Lynette Galloway, RN, and Mildred Jackson, RN, founded the organization as a forum to *investigate, define, and determine the healthcare needs of Black Americans with cancer.* Dr. Murphy urged the staff to address cancer issues in minorities in their programs.

The first clinical trials conducted in the United States on tumor necrosis factor were conducted at Roswell Park. Dr. John Black, Department of Experimental Biology, was a member of an international panel of independent researchers which announced that U.S. and Canadian residents living around the Great Lakes faced heavier doses of toxic chemicals in drinking water and food than anywhere else in North America. Despite demonstrating that the problem had been around for at least a decade, the group maintained that *few concrete corrective measures have been implemented to radically deal with serious toxic contamination at four dozen toxic hot spots such as the Niagara River, the Buffalo River, and scores of other urban sites from Green Bay, Wisconsin to Hamilton, Ontario.* The group urged North American governments to develop a comprehensive toxic substance management strategy.

**8-26.**
Dr. Thomas Dougherty,
pioneer of photodynamic
therapy (PDT).

**8-25.**
Dr. Jack Black exploring
cancer in fish similar to
what Dr. Gaylord did.

Based on technology developed by Roswell Park scientists, particularly Dr. Thomas J. Dougherty, the first computer-controlled laser for photodynamic therapy was manufactured and marketed by a Japanese firm. This new laser represented the most successful example of the Institute's technology development program and scientific collaboration with industry.

At the same time, the Institute was expanding its long-recognized leadership role through national and international collaborations represented at Roswell Park. Dr. Murphy promoted and nurtured these efforts based on the philosophy that the function of the clinical staff was to improve clinical treatment through cooperative groups and individual clinical research. He urged very early, before others, that minority groups and the elderly be included in clinical research. Consequently, many of the clinical staff were sharing clinical research with the following national and international groups.

- Pediatric Oncology Group
- National Bladder Cancer Group
- National Prostatic Cancer Project
- Radiation Therapy Oncology Group
- National Wilms' Tumor Study Group
- Intergroup Rhabdomyosarcoma Study
- Eastern Cooperative Oncology Group
- Gastrointestinal Tumor Study Group
- NCI Centralized Cancer Patient Data System
- Gynecologic Oncology Group
  Statistical office
- Organ System Coordinating Center
- National Cooperative Drug Discovery Group
- UICC International Cancer Patient Data
  Exchange System
- Multiple Sclerosis Interferon Study and
  MS/IF Statistical Office
- Cancer and Leukemia Group B and CALGB
  Pathology Coordinating Office

As a result of establishing the Cancer Prevention-Detection Center, more than 200 cancers were discovered during routine screening—the highest number reported during a single year. Over 6,000 Western New Yorkers were screened in 1985. The Department of Education mobilized senior citizens groups through educational outreach programs to seek screening and treatment at Roswell Park. It was a very successful proactive effort.

8-27.
Certificate given to
President Nixon by
Dr. Murphy on behalf
of the Institute for
sponsoring the
National Cancer
Act of 1971.

There were a number of special events which occurred during this period in the history of the Institute which are noteworthy to mention.

The year 1971 was historic not only at the Institute, but nationally. The National Cancer Act of 1971 was passed, marshaling for the first time federal resources in a concentrated fight against cancer. Roswell Park played a major role in getting the National Cancer Act passed. Dr. Gerald P. Murphy had invited the United States House of Representatives to hold hearings on the proposed legislation at the Institute. The hearings were held October 11, 1971 at the Institute. Dr. Murphy, Dr. Mirand, Dr. Moore, and others testified to urge passage of the National Cancer Act. In addition, Dr. Murphy and Dr. Mirand lobbied cancer centers in the United States to gain their support for the National Cancer Act of 1971.

Mr. Thaddeus J. Dulski, then Congressman of the Forty-first District, welcomed his legislative colleagues to Roswell Park, saying: *We in Buffalo are proud of Roswell Park Memorial Institute. It is the oldest and one of the largest cancer institutes in the world. From these laboratories, down through the years, have come many discoveries and developments in the desperate fight to find a cure for cancer.*

Representative Paul G. Rogers (D-Florida), chairman of the subcommittee and one of the supporters of the National Cancer Act, stated at the hearings that it was *very unusual to hold hearings away from Congress in Washington, D.C., but it was the pioneering effort seventy-three years ago of the Institute that demonstrated the role of government to support cancer research and treatment.* He summed up the hearings at the Institute by thanking Dr. Murphy and the staff for *showing us what a comprehensive cancer center should be. . . . Now, our subcommittee must decree legislation which will accomplish what you have done here on a nationwide basis. The thoughts you have given us here today will help us in drawing up that legislation.*

To

## President Richard Milhous Nixon

The staff of Roswell Park Memorial Institute takes this opportunity to acknowledge your contribution in strengthening the national effort to conquer cancer and in making the conquest of cancer a national goal of the highest priority.

With the National Cancer Act of 1971 Cancer Institutes like Roswell Park Memorial Institute and other health facilities in the United States of America are able to develop scientific knowledge and to coordinate their respective activities and resources needed to treat and control cancer. We are most grateful for your support.

Roswell Park Memorial Institute
Buffalo, New York
October 15, 1972

Gerald P. Murphy
Institute Director

In a report of the hearing published in the Congressional Record, Representative Dulski quoted a statement from Dr. James T. Grace, Jr.: *If I had a choice between a moon walk and the life of a single child with leukemia, I would never glance upward.*

The legislation which emerged from Congress, the National Cancer Act, was signed into law by President Richard M. Nixon December 23, 1971, in the East Room of the White House, with Dr. Murphy present.

President Nixon signed the Institute Guest Book January 13, 1972, at a White House ceremony celebrating the signing of the Act. On March 7, 1972, as a result of the Institute's effort to see the bill passed, President Nixon appointed Dr. Murphy to the eighteen-member, newly created National Cancer Advisory Board as provided for in Public Law 92-218, the National Cancer Act of 1971.

**8-29.**

Dr. Murphy, appointed to
the first National Cancer
Advisory Board by
President Nixon.
Dr. Murphy is the fifth
from the right.

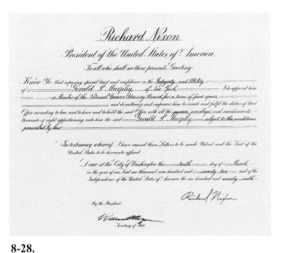

**8-28.**

Letter from President
Nixon appointing
Dr. Murphy to National
Cancer Advisory Board.

The Association for Research of Childhood Cancer (AROCC) was organized. This group, composed of parents of children who have died of cancer, makes annual contributions to Roswell Park for research carried out in the Department of Pediatrics. The organization received its charter in the summer of 1971.

Roswell Park expanded its national leadership role against cancer in 1973, when Dr. Gerald P. Murphy was appointed first national chairman of the Cancer Control Advisory Program, which was created under the National Cancer Act. During his four-year term, the Program grew from an initial breast screening bilateral program with the American Cancer Society, at a $2 million level, to a multifaceted program exceeding $90 million, and affecting many cities, institutions, health departments, and regional areas of the United States.

In 1973 Roswell Park celebrated seventy-five years of pioneering cancer research, treatment, and education. The milestone was celebrated by over 900 people May 2 at the Hotel Statler Hilton. United States Congressman Paul G. Rogers was the main speaker. The Seventy-fifth Anniversary Committee was chaired by Mr. Gerald Saltarelli and co-chaired by Mrs. David Loeb. Members of the Committee included: Dr. E. A. Mirand, Mrs. Gerald P. Murphy, Mrs. Bruce E. Wallis (granddaughter of Edward H. Butler, Sr.), Mr. Alfred Kirchhofer, Mr. Elmer Lux, Mrs. Walter T. Mahoney, Mr. James L. Crane, Jr. (grandson of Mrs. Gratwick), Mrs. Byron Koekkoek (granddaughter of Dr. Park), and others. A symposium was also held to commemorate the Seventy-fifth Anniversary. The publication that resulted, PERSPECTIVES IN CANCER RESEARCH AND TREATMENT, by Gerald P. Murphy, editor, and Dr. David Pressman and Dr. Mirand, associate editors, was published by Alan R. Liss, New York City, in 1973. Sixty-two staff members contributed to this work. In addition, the MEDICAL WORLD NEWS (September 7, 1973), the journal CANCER RESEARCH, and the BUFFALO EVENING NEWS published feature articles on Roswell Park.

**8-30.**
Dr. Murphy had good contacts at the White House with President Nixon. His daughter, Julie Nixon Eisenhower, visited the Institute in 1972 with Congressman Jack Kemp (right of J.N. Eisenhower).

**8-31.**
Seventy-fifth Commemorative Mural paying tribute to medical research and education was designed and painted by RPCI employee Tasha Turk, and is located in Lobby of Research Studies Center.

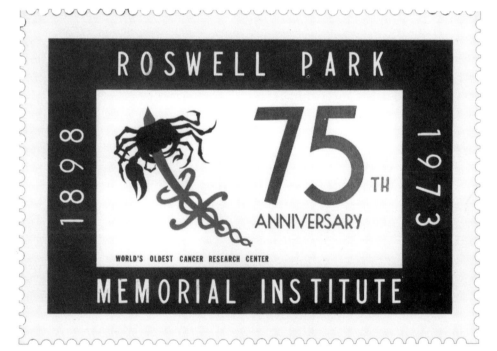

**8-32.**
In honor of the Seventy-fifth Anniversary of the founding of the Roswell Park Cancer Institute, a Commemorative Stamp was suggested by Joanne Townsend of the Institute. The stamp and a similar postal meter slug, designed by Tasha Turk, were used for our routine mailing during 1973.

**8-33**

On May 2, 1973, at the Hotel Statler in Buffalo over 900 people from staff, national cancer community, and the local community celebrated Seventy-fifth Anniversary of RPCI. Congressman Paul Rogers, co-sponsor of National Cancer Act of 1971, was the main speaker. He acknowl- edged the Institute's efforts in helping to pass this Act. Left to right: Mr. A. Kirchhofer, Dr. G. Moore, Mr. E.V. Regan, Dr. Murphy, State Health Commissioner Dr. Hollis Ingraham, Congressman P. Rogers.

In July, 1974, the auditorium in the Research Studies Center was officially named the Herman E. Hilleboe Auditorium, in honor of Dr. Herman E. Hilleboe, whose efforts as New York State Health Commissioner in the early 1950s were instrumental in expanding the Institute's mission and enhancing its national and international repu- tation. Roswell Park Memorial Institute owes much of its present stature to the dynamic energy and cooperations of Dr. Hilleboe.

Dr. Donald S. Coffey presented the first Roswell Park Lecture on February 7, 1978. This lecture series celebrates the diversified interests and expertise of Dr. Park. Dr. Coffey, professor of pharmacology and experimental therapeutics at Johns Hopkins School of Medicine, spoke on the Continuing Development of Man.

**8-34**
Assemblyman Chester
Hardt, a great friend
of the Institute during
Dr. Murphy's administra-
tion, at the Seventy-fifth
Anniversary Gala.

THE WHITE HOUSE
WASHINGTON

June 21, 1974

Dear Dr. Murphy:

Before any more time passes, I want to take
the opportunity to thank you for your kind letter
of May 11, noting the approaching end of Roswell
Park Memorial Institute's 75th Anniversary year.
We in this Administration are extremely proud
and grateful that we had a role in the implemen-
tation of the National Cancer Act of 1971. As
you know, that Act has expanded Federal support
of the cancer research and control effort to unprecedented proportions.

It is an honor for both my daughter Julie and me
to have our signatures permanently inscribed in
your Institutional Guest Book. The accomplishments
of the Roswell Park Memorial Institute -- not only
in its service to cancer patients and their families,
but in its many fruitful research studies in the prevention and control of malignant disease -- have
commanded the utmost respect among medical
professionals and laymen alike throughout the
world.

Also I want to personally congratulate you for your
service on the National Cancer Advisory Board.
If it were not for the expert and unselfish contributions of you and your colleagues on the Board,

our present high hopes for the success of the
National Cancer Program would be consider-
ably darkened.

With my appreciation and my best wishes,

Sincerely,

*Richard Nixon*

Gerald P. Murphy, M. D.
Institute Director
Roswell Park Memorial Institute
666 Elm Street
Buffalo, New York 14203

**8-35.**
President Nixon sent
a letter on June 21, 1974,
acknowledging the
Seventy-fifth Anniversary
of RPCI and his
daughter's pleasure as
a signee in Institute's
Guest Book and for Dr.
Murphy's contributions
on the National Cancer
Advisory Board.

The Dr. William H. Wehr Award was established in 1978 to recognize the contributions of senior staff members to the development of Roswell Park. Dr. Merrill A. Bender, chief of Nuclear Medicine, was the first recipient for his pioneering work in nuclear medicine and radiology, particularly radioisotopic detection of tumors.

Dr. Gerald Murphy was granted a private audience with Pope John Paul II in the Vatican, at which he presented mementos of Roswell Park and the cities of Buffalo and Niagara Falls to His Holiness. He also presented a white and gold leather binder containing the American Cancer Society's Sword of Hope, with the following inscription: *We salute your magnificent compassion for all humankind and your efforts to join together those who understand the life force of the spirit in maintaining the health of the world.* Pope John Paul II extended his blessing to the staff for continuing its battle to conquer cancer.

Significant progress in cancer research and treatment was made during the administration of Dr. Murphy, and the staff received national and international recognition for their work.

Dr. James F. Holland was elected president of the American Association for Cancer Research, the ninth Roswell Park staff member so honored.

Dr. Edmund Klein, chief of Dermatology, developed a protocol for the application of a highly effective topical anticancer agent, 5-Fluorouracil (5-FU) for the treatment of skin cancer in 1970.

In 1972 Photodynamic Therapy, a laser/chemical cancer treatment pioneered by Dr. Thomas J. Dougherty, was used worldwide—as an investigational therapy—to treat cancers of the skin, breast, lung, bladder, esophagus, and head and neck.

Also in 1972 Roswell Park became headquarters of the National Prostatic Cancer Project, under the direction of Dr. Gerald P. Murphy. One of only three Organ Site Projects initiated by the National Cancer Institute that year, the objective was to identify and evaluate specific chemotherapeutic agents which might be useful in treating prostatic cancer.

**8-36.**
Hilleboe family at the dedication of the Hilleboe Auditorium on July 19, 1974.

Childhood cancer was still resisting the advances made in cancer research and treatment over the years. Survival rates were hovering around a dismal 50 percent. However, in 1975 this began to change. Dr. Lucius Sinks, chief of Pediatrics, and his colleague Dr. Arnold I. Freeman, were the first to use high doses of the drug methotrexate to treat pediatric tumors. This treatment alone has improved the survival rates from childhood leukemia worldwide.

Around the same time, Dr. T. Ming Chu and his associates characterized a human prostate-specific antigen. Through the transfer of the patented technology, this tumor marker—the most effective parameter in the measurement of prostate cancer—is now widely used in the United States and abroad. Their discovery also led to the development of the PSA test which is used in PSA-based screening for the early detection of prostate cancer.

At an annual meeting of the International Union Against Cancer (UICC), in Florence, Italy, in October 1974 Dr. Murphy became one of the first Americans to be appointed secretary-general. The UICC is the only non-governmental, international voluntary organization devoted solely to promoting the campaign against cancer. That same year, Dr. Murphy was appointed president of the New York State Chapter of the American Cancer Society.

Dr. Michael Laskowski received the 1980 Dr. William H. Wehr Award for his studies on nucleolytic and proteolytic enzymes.

The possible association between heredity and some types of cancer was being reported in the scientific literature at this time. Dr. M. Steven Piver, chief of Gynecologic Oncology, established the Familial Ovarian Cancer Registry in 1981. This national tracking system stores the names of women with a strong family history of ovarian cancer and advises them as to their risk of developing the disease and methods of prevention.

Dr. Gerald P. Murphy received the Silver Medal from the European Organization for Treatment and Research on Cancer in 1981 for *outstanding contributions to the treatment of prostate cancer as chairman of the National Prostatic Cancer Project and for work achieved at Roswell Park Memorial Institute* in 1981. He was also elected president-elect of the national American Cancer Society and of the Society of Surgical Oncology, which was founded in 1940 as the James Ewing Society. Dr. C. William Aungst was elected vice president/president-elect of the New York State Division of the American Cancer Society that same year. Dr. John W. Pickren, chief of the Pathology Department, received the 1981 Dr. William H. Wehr Award.

**8-37.**
Dr. T. M. Chu developed the PSA Test.

Roswell Park Cancer Institute was cited as one of the top three cancer centers in the United States by Business Week magazine.

In 1982 Dr. Mirand, as Secretary-General of the UICC's Thirteenth International Cancer Congress sponsored by Roswell Park and the Fred Hutchinson Cancer Centers, organized one of the most successful international cancer congresses held in Seattle, Washington, September 8–15. (Like the Olympic Games, UICC Congresses are highly sought after by countries on a fiercely competitive basis.) Over 10,000 cancer researchers participated in the Congress. The five-volume proceedings were published by Alan R. Liss of New York City. The International Cancer Congress would have been held in Buffalo but the city lacked the facilities at that time to accommodate such a large gathering.

The early 1980s was also a period of significant improvements in treating colorectal cancer, malignant melanoma, and soft tissue sarcoma. Dr. Maire T. Hakala pioneered the development of the drug combination 5-FU and leucovorin. Today, clinical trials with this treatment indicate an increase in the response rate of patients with colorectal carcinomas —from 15 percent to 45 percent. Roswell Park's Department of Surgical Oncology reported one of the country's lowest recurrence rate colorectal—10 percent at five years; one of the highest survival rates for malignant melanoma at five years—81 percent; and new surgical techniques which saved the limbs of over 95 percent of soft tissue sarcoma patients. In fact, Roswell Park performs the fewest cancer-related amputations in the nation. However, for those patients in whom amputation is unavoidable, Roswell Park established an Amputee Clinic for their care within the Rehabilitation and Continuing Care Department in 1981.

The Cancer Information Service sponsored by the National Cancer Institute began at Roswell Park in August 1976. The toll-free telephone counseling and information service puts callers from all areas of New York State, except New York City, in contact with trained staff who answer questions and provide information on cancer topics. By 1982 CIS had received 60,000 calls, and by the early 1990s the service area had been expanded to include Western Pennsylvania.

115

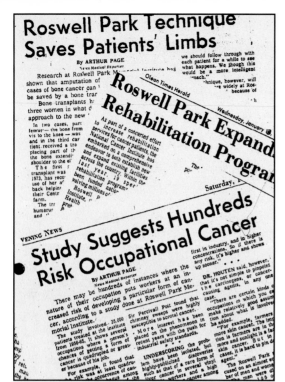

**8-38.**
Newspaper clippings indicate progress in cancer findings by staff.

**8-39.**
Dr. Mirand, as secretary-general, addressing participants at the Opening of the Thirteenth International Cancer Congress of the UICC in Seattle, Washington, in 1982.

**8-40.**
Dr. and Mrs. G. P. Murphy, Dr. Mirand, with Professor Karl Schmidt of Germany at the UICC International Congress.

In 1983 Roswell Park researchers continued to be recognized for their research and treatment advances. Institute clinicians expanded the application of photodynamic therapy, already proven to be highly effective in treating skin and subcutaneous lesions, to less accessible tumors, such as the stomach and esophagus.

Dr. M. Steven Piver, chief of Gynecologic Oncology, reported, for the first time, the significant role of the drug hydroxyurea in enhancing the effects of radiation in patients with cervical cancer. Patients treated with radiation and hydroxyurea sustain five-year survival rates of 94 percent compared to 53 percent in patients receiving radiation and a placebo. The results of these breakthrough studies were presented at the nineteenth annual May meetings of the American Society of Clinical Oncology in San Diego and received national media attention.

Dr. Dutzu Rosner, associate chief of the Department of Breast Surgery, provided convincing first-time evidence that brain metastases in patients with breast cancer could be treated with systemic chemotherapy. This research dispelled the widely-held belief that standard chemotherapeutic drugs delivered through the bloodstream would not penetrate the blood brain barrier and reach the metastases.

**8-41.**
Longtime friends of the Institute going back to the Kress administration who offered financial assistance to graduate students to attend the UICC International Cancer Congress in Budapest. Left to right: Mrs. Marge Lazar, Mrs. Sylvia Hinerfeld, Dr. Louis Lazar, Dr. Amy Mirand, Dr. E. A. Mirand, and Mr. E. M. Frantz. Dr. Joseph DiPaolo is in background (right).

**8-42.**
Marilyn Quayle, wife
of Vice President Dan
Quayle, visits Cancer
Information Service at
Roswell Park in 1991.
Mrs. Quayle is with
Dr. Sherri Darrow,
and Ramon Melendez
is at extreme left.

Drs. Julius Horosewicz, Susan Leong, and Edwin A. Mirand developed a technique that increased the yield of highly purified human beta interferon. Prior to this, few places, even pharmaceutical companies, were able to produce an effective human interferon. The American Cancer Society provided funds to Dr. Mirand so that Roswell Park could manufacture this type of interferon for distribution to scientists worldwide for human clinical trials.

A team of international researchers, including Dr. Susan Naylor of the Department of Human Genetics, identified the genetic pattern linked to Huntington's disease. This breakthrough, which enabled physicians to diagnose the disorder earlier and determine its genetic transfer, was published in NATURE.

Dr. Elias Cohen, director of the Blood Bank, discovered an antibody in the blood of whales and dolphins that provided important insight into human disease remission and relapse, as well as changes in the immune response during disease, infection, and malignancy.

Roswell Park resumed its autologous bone marrow transplant program.

Another national feather in Roswell Park's cap came in 1984 when the Institute won a *spirited competition* for the Organ Systems Coordinating Center (OSCC), sponsored by the National Cancer Institute. The National Cancer Advisory Board voted in favor of Roswell Park over the University of Texas Graduate School of Biomedical Sciences. The Board's action came after a heated discussion in closed session. The initial review group had scored the Texas application nine points higher than Roswell Park's. However, some Board members felt that scores that close left the issue entirely up to the Board. Dr. Gerald Murphy's effective leadership of the National Prostatic Cancer Project, one of five Projects (bladder, breast, prostate, large bowel, pancreas) in the old Organ Site Program, was a major factor in the Board's final decision. The OSCC was awarded $900,000 a year for five years to coordinate the Program. Dr. Murphy, the only Organ Site Program chairman to compete for the coordinating center grant, was named principal investigator, Dr. James Karr was named chief coordinator and liaison with the Prostate Cancer Working Group, and Dr. Clement Ip, of the Breast Surgery Department, was named liaison for the Breast Cancer Working Group.

Immunologist Dr. Heinz Kohler developed the first anti-idiotypic vaccine against *streptococcus pneumoniae* infection by applying the Jerne theory of the immune network. This method of vaccine production was inexpensive, allowed for larger, purer quantities, and spawned research to develop a vaccine against tumor-specific antigens. This research continues at Roswell Park today.

Nicotinomide adenine dinucleotide (NAD) had long been considered by scientists as the single-most important co-enzyme because of its involvement in dehydrogenase reactions. Crystallographers worldwide had been struggling to determine the structure of NAD for more than two decades. In 1984 scientists in the Center for Crystallographic Research at Roswell Park succeeded.

Drs. Kailash Chadha and Eugene Sulkowski, Department of Cell & Tumor Biology, received a U.S. patent for their new method of producing and purifying human leukocyte interferon on a large scale. Dr. Zenon Gibas, Department of Human Genetics, was a member of an international team of scientists that identified the marker for transitional cell carcinoma of the bladder on chromosome 11.

A number of staff members at this time, including Institute Director Dr. Gerald P. Murphy, received regional, national, and international recognition. For instance, at the seventieth meeting of the American Cancer Society, in New York City, Dr. Murphy became the first volunteer from the New York State Division to be elected national president of the organization. He also was elected chairman of the Executive Council of Society of Surgical Oncology.

Dr. Harold O. Douglass, Jr., chief of the Upper Gastrointestinal and Endoscopy Service, was elected chairman of the Gastrointestinal Tumor Study Group, the first organized national effort devoted to the research and treatment of gastrointestinal tumors. Dr. George Collins, chief of Cardiology, was appointed to a three-year term on the Board of Trustees of the American Medical Association. Dr. Edwin A. Mirand, associate Institute director for Educational Affairs, was one of fourteen experts appointed by Governor Mario Cuomo to serve on the New York State AIDS Advisory Panel in 1982 and remains on this panel in 1998.

Dr. C. William Aungst, associate director of Clinical Affairs, was elected president, and Dr. Norman G. Schaaf, chief of the Department of Dentistry & Maxillofacial Prosthetics, was elected director-at-large of the New York State Division of the American Cancer Society.

Allen Doster, a West Seneca resident and Roswell Park blood donor, was listed in the 1983 Guinness Book of World Records as holding the record for voluntary blood platelet donations. (His name has appeared in the record book from 1983 until the present.)

The Department of Cancer Control & Epidemiology, under the direction of Dr. Curtis J. Mettlin, released an important report which, for the first time, described and assessed the cancer incidence and mortality patterns in the eight western counties of New York State. Based on 1980 census data, CANCER IN WESTERN NEW YORK 1980 revealed that the regional incidence rates for lung and colorectal cancers exceeded the national average. In late 1984 the same group reported that the nation's five-year survival rate for prostate cancer had improved dramatically since 1978, with about 13,000 more men—both black and white—surviving all clinical stages of the disease. The report also pointed to a developing national trend toward earlier prostate cancer detection. Their reports were received favorably.

Roswell Park staff members continued to have a national presence by serving on oncology boards and receiving recognition for research and clinical efforts. President Ronald Reagan appointed Dr. Enrico Mihich, director of the Department of Experimental Therapeutics, to a six-year term on the National Cancer Advisory Board. Dr. M. Steven Piver, deputy chief of the Department of Gynecologic Oncology, was elected honorary fellow of the Texas Association of Obstetricians and Gynecologists. Dr. Thomas Dao, chief of the Department of Breast Surgery, was appointed to the National Task Force on Breast Cancer Control of the American Cancer Society. Dr. Edward Henderson, chief of the Department of Medicine, and Dr. M. Steven Piver were listed among "The Best Medical Specialists in the U.S." in TOWN AND COUNTRY MAGAZINE. Dr. David Harker, *the father of x-ray crystallography,* was awarded the Gregory Aminoff Medal in Gold by the Royal Swedish Academy of Sciences in recognition of his *fundamental contributions to the development of methods for determining molecular structures of biologically important substances.*

The Institute's proven track record of excellence in research and treatment was further reinforced. A government report indicated that Buffalo, New York, captured 13 percent of all National Institutes of Health grants awarded to New York State in 1983. In addition, Roswell Park was named one of the nation's top three cancer hospitals in GOOD HOUSEKEEPING's annual listing of the "Best Hospitals in America."

Dr. Herbert Hauptman, president and research director of the Medical Foundation of Buffalo, Inc. and professor of Biophysics in the Roswell Park Graduate Division, won the Nobel Prize in chemistry with Dr. Jerome Karle for the discovery of the Direct Methods, a way of determining three-dimensional crystal structures of complex molecules. The now-standard technique makes it possible to identify and design new drugs, resulting in the saving of millions of lives.

Dr. Thomas Shows, director of the Department of Human Genetics, was elected fellow of the American Association for the Advancement of Science, and Dr. Curtis Mettlin, director of Cancer Control and Epidemiology, was elected to a two-year term as medical director-at-large of the American Cancer Society.

Like any organization, changes result in making many appointments. Dr. Murphy responded very effectively in making appointments despite the difficulties he encountered in the later years of his administration with State hiring freezes and policy differences with the New York State Commissioner of Health.

In 1970 Dr. Joseph Barlow was appointed chief of the Gynecology Department, replacing the late Dr. John Graham. Dr. James F. Holland was the ninth Roswell Park staff member to serve as the president of the AACR.

Mrs. Eva M. B. Noles who had served in various capacities in the Department of Nursing at the Institute since 1945, was appointed director of Nursing in 1971, replacing Mr. Charles E. Martin. At this time, the Institute had 329 beds and a nursing staff of 350.

New appointments at Roswell Park Cancer Institute during this period of time included: Dr. Enrico Mihich, director of Experimental Therapeutics and director of the Cancer Drug Center, and Dr. Fred Rosen, associate director of the Cancer Drug Center, in January 1971; Dr. E. Douglas Holyoke, chief of General Surgery, in February 1971; and Dr. Ronald G. Vincent as chief of Thoracic Surgery, in July 1971. Dr. Mihich, Dr. Holyoke, Dr. Vincent, and Mrs. Noles had been on the Roswell Park staff for a number of years.

Dr. C. William Aungst was appointed associate Institute director for Clinical Affairs in 1974. Dr. Aungst, who had served in various capacities since joining the Institute staff in 1960, filled the position that had been vacant since the retirement of Dr. Wehr. His mother, Anna V. Aungst, had retired in 1967 after thirty-one years of devoted service to Roswell Park. She died in 1974, but was happy and proud that she lived to see her son become associate Institute director.

Dr. Hollis S. Ingraham retired as New York State Health Commissioner January 16, 1975, and was succeeded by Dr. Robert P. Whalen, who had been deputy commissioner for ten years. Dr. Ingraham had maintained as active a relationship with Roswell Park as had his predecessor, Dr. Herman Hilleboe. His untiring interest provided major contributions to program development and physical expansion. Dr. Whalen proved to be the same.

Dr. David Harker, director of Biophysics and the Center for Crystallographic Research, retired in 1976, and was elected to the National Academy of Sciences. Dr. Harold C. Box was named director of Biophysics. Dr. H. James Wallace, Jr., succeeded Dr. Aungst as director of Cancer Control.

The National Cancer Act had formalized, in its definition of a comprehensive cancer center, a cancer control component which had been in place for a number of years at the Institute. To reaffirm the Institute's commitment to cancer control, Dr. Murphy charged Dr. H. James Wallace, Jr., with responsibilities for continued development and supervision of efforts to extend the work of the Roswell Park staff beyond the walls of the Institute.

Today, the Institute's formal outreach programs encompass a broad spectrum of cancer control efforts: prevention programs against lung cancer, skin cancer, and exposure to carcinogenic agents; screening and detection of cervical cancers; regional diagnosis and treatment efforts through a toll-free consultation telephone service; participation in cancer programs at community hospitals; professional education programs; and a comprehensive rehabilitation center.

**8-44.**
Left to right: Mrs. Eva Noles, Miss Patricia Burns, and Miss Ethel Chandler at the dedication of the Ethel Chandler Conference Room.

Some of the other major appointments at the Institute and elsewhere having an impact on the Institute during Dr. Murphy's administration included: Dr. Claude Merrin, chief of Urology; Dr. Ethelyn Jennings, chief of Diagnostic Radiology; Dr. Josef Vana, director of Epidemiology; Dr. Charles West, chief of Neurosurgery; Dr. John Fitzpatrick, chief of Laboratory Medicine; Dr. Richard Johnson, chief of Radiation Medicine; and Dr. Edward Henderson, chief of Medicine A. The retirement of Dr. Theodore S. Hauschka, world renowned cancer biologist, resulted in the appointment of Dr. Charles Helmstetter as director of Experimental Biology.

Since the arrival of the first patient in 1914, the Department of Nursing had grown along with the number of patients, until today when it is the largest single department in Roswell Park. Each of the previous Nursing directors have embraced the highest ideals to which the nursing profession is dedicated: Miss Katherine H. Danner(1914–1915), Mrs. L.M. Weinland (1923–1924), Miss Louise Merwin (1924–1943), Miss Grace Scharlou (1944–1945), Miss Ethel Chandler (1945–1960), Miss Mary K. Crook (1960–1962), Mr. Charles E. Martin (1962–1971), and Mrs. Eva M. B. Noles (1971–1974). Miss Patricia Burns (1974–1982), who had served as Assistant Director of Nursing Education for seventeen years, was appointed director of Nursing in 1974 following the retirement of Mrs. Noles, who had served at Roswell Park for twenty-seven years.

Dr. Michael P. McGarry was appointed supervisor of the Springville Biological Laboratories. Dr. Arnold I. Freeman was named chief of Pediatrics in 1977, replacing Dr. Lucius Sinks. Dr. T. Ming Chu was appointed director of the newly formed Diagnostic Immunology Department.

In 1978 Dr. Edwin A. Mirand was appointed secretary-general of the Thirteenth International Cancer Congress by the International Union Against Cancer (UICC), in recognition of his contributions to cancer research and education. This position is highly sought after by countries around the world.

Mr. Peter J. Crotty, Sr., was elected chairman of the seven-member Board of Visitors in July 1978. Mr. Crotty, a prominent attorney and former president of the Buffalo Common Council, was appointed to the Board of Visitors in 1976 by Governor Hugh L. Carey. Mr. Crotty served as a trustee of the Statler Foundation since 1962, and as its chairman since 1972.

Dr. David Axelrod was appointed by newly elected Governor Mario M. Cuomo to succeed Dr. Robert Whalen as New York State commissioner of health on January 2, 1979. Dr. Axelrod had been the director of Laboratories and Research in the New York State Health Department prior to his appointment, and received prominence for his handling of the Love Canal Project in Niagara Falls, New York.

There were a number of changes at Roswell Park in 1979. Dr. Joseph Sokal, chief of Medicine B, retired. The department was renamed the Clinical Pharmacology and Therapeutics Department under the direction of Dr. Patrick J. Creaven. Dr. Sokal received the Dr. William H. Wehr Award for his contributions. Medicine A was renamed Medical Oncology and Dr. Edward S. Henderson was appointed chief. Medicine C was renamed Genetics and Endocrinology, with Dr. Avery A. Sandberg continuing as chief. Dr. Fred Rosen was appointed associate Institute director for Scientific Affairs, succeeding Dr. David Pressman, who had resigned to devote all of his energies to directing the Immunology and Immunochemistry Department. Dr. Curtis J. Mettlin was appointed director of the Cancer Control and Epidemiology Department. Dr. J. Edson Pontes was appointed chief of the Urologic Oncology.

**8-46**
Dr. Gerald
Murphy with NYS
Commissioner of Health
Dr. David Axelrod.

Dr. Timothy E. O'Connor was named associated director for Scientific Affairs in 1981, following the retirement of Dr. Fred Rosen, who had a long career at the Institute which began in the Department of Experimental Therapeutics. Other significant appointments in 1981 included: Dr. Edward W. Bockstahler as director of Clinics, responsible for the Employees Clinic, the Cancer Prevention and Detection Clinic, and the Rehabilitation and Continuing Care Department; Dr. Heinz Kohler replaced the late Dr. David Pressman as director of the Immunology and Immunochemistry Department and changed the name to Molecular Immunology; and Dr. Frederick Helm was appointed as chief of Dermatology.

Bone marrow transplantation had shown promise as a treatment for certain forms of cancer, and in some cases, aplastic anemia and combined immune deficiencies in children. There were only a few centers in the United States performing this procedure. Patients from Buffalo who might benefit from a bone marrow transplant had to travel, in most cases, to other states. To address this problem, Roswell Park opened the Bone Marrow Transplant Center April 2, 1982, as a referral center under the direction of Dr. Donald J. Higby.

New appointments and promotions in 1983 included: Georgia M. Burnette, RN, MS, former associate director of Nursing Services at Buffalo General Hospital, was appointed director of Nursing, replacing Patricia E. Burns, RN, MS, who retired in 1981; Dr. Hiroshi Takita, was promoted to chief of the Department of Thoracic Surgery; and Dr. Ole Holtermann was promoted to chief of the Department of Dermatology.

**8-47.**
Staff members during Dr. Murphy's administration welcoming Professor Mathé from Paris, France, February 1985.

**8-48.**
Mrs. Ann Geraci and
Director of Nursing
Mrs. Georgia Burnette
discuss breast self-
examination models.

The scientific world was saddened by the loss of two of its most respected and talented pioneers. Dr. Abraham Lilienfeld, the *Father of Contemporary Chronic Disease Epidemiology* died August 6, 1984, at the age of sixty-three. From 1954 to 1958, Dr. Lilienfeld established and chaired the Department of Statistics and Epidemiological Research at Roswell Park. Dr. Lilienfeld was instrumental in expanding epidemiology from a discipline focused on infectious diseases to one embracing chronic diseases, such as cancer, heart disease, stroke, cerebral palsy, and epilepsy. Much of his research focused on cerebrovascular diseases, occupational carcinogens and possible relation between the endocrine system and various forms of cancer. At the time of his death, he was chairman *pro tem* of the Department of Behavioral Sciences at Johns Hopkins University.

Dr. Carl Cori, the biochemist who shared the Nobel Prize in Medicine with his wife Gerty in 1947, died on October 19, 1984 at the age of eighty-seven. The Coris had done much of their early research at Roswell Park.

Two department heads were named in early 1985. Dr. Robert P. Huben was appointed chief of the Department of Urologic Oncology, replacing Dr. J. Edson Pontes, and Dr. Jaya Ghoorah was appointed chief of the Department of Diagnostic Radiology, succeeding Dr. Ethelyn Jennings, who had retired. A new Phillips mammography unit—the first of its kind in Western New York—was installed in the Diagnostic Radiology Department.

**8-49.**
Staff members welcome
Professor E. Robinson
from Israel in 1983.

Despite all of the progress made during Dr. Murphy's administration, New York State Health Commissioner Dr. David Axelrod, in early July 1984, convened a six-member blue-ribbon panel of cancer experts to review Roswell Park activities. The results of their year-long evaluation of the Institute's administration, research, patient care, and educational programs were contained in their report, THE FUTURE OF ROSWELL PARK CANCER INSTITUTE. The panel called for restructuring the Institute's governance and management and the development of a long-term strategic plan that would redefine the role of the Institute as a national and regional cancer center. Assemblyman Chester Hardt and others responding in published articles in the BUFFALO NEWS felt the report was politically motivated.

From the composition of the review panel, Dr. Murphy realized very early his fate, and on July 30, 1985, he resigned as director of Roswell Park due to programmatic differences starting with opposing the move of Roswell Park's clinical facilities to Buffalo General Hospital which Commissioner of Health Dr. David Axelrod endorsed. He accepted the position of director of Oncological Research Programs in Urology at the State University of New York at Buffalo. Later, he served as senior vice president for the National Office of the American Cancer Society. Much of what Dr. Murphy urged to be done came later in the Major Modernization Project in Dr. Thomas B. Tomasi's administration. In announcing Dr. Murphy's resignation, Health Commissioner Dr. David Axelrod said, *In his fifteen years as director, Dr. Murphy guided the Institute through a period of major expansion and research accomplishment. His active participation in the American Cancer Society and other national and international associations dedicated to cancer research helped to attract millions of dollars in grant funds to advance research, patient care, and educational programs at Roswell Park Memorial Institute.*

**9-1.**
Dr. John Wright,
Mr. Peter J. Crotty, Sr.,
Mayor James Griffin,
and Dr. Murphy.

# Chapter 9

# A Brief Interlude:
## The Wright Year

Following Dr. Murphy's resignation, the New York State Department of Health announced new administrative appointments at Roswell Park: Dr. John R. Wright, head of the Department of Pathology at Buffalo General Hospital and a member of Roswell Park's Board of Visitors, was appointed interim director; Dr. Andrew A. Gage was appointed associate Institute director for Clinical Affairs, replacing Dr. C. William Aungst; Dr. Verne Chapman was appointed associate Institute director of Scientific Affairs, replacing Dr. Timothy O'Connor; Mr. Robert E. Lawson was appointed hospital director; and Dr. Edwin A. Mirand remained as associate Institute director for Educational Affairs. Commissioner of Health Axelrod re-emphasized the State's *continuous commitment* to Roswell Park, indicating that the transfer of inpatients' beds to Buffalo General Hospital was no longer an option.

In addition, Dr. Arthur H. K. Djang was appointed associate chief of the Laboratory Medicine Department; Dr. John Gaeta, former director of the Tissue Pathology Laboratory at Buffalo General Hospital, was appointed chief of the Pathology Department; and Dr. James Karr replaced Dr. Murphy as interim director of the Organ Systems Coordinating Center.

In 1985 the Institute was saddened by the deaths of Dr. Richard J. R. Johnson, chairman of the Department of Radiation Medicine since 1974, on October 14; Patricia E. Burns, RN, director of Nursing from 1974 to 1982, on December 4; and Alfred Kirchhofer, retired managing editor of the BUFFALO EVENING NEWS and a member of the Institute's Board of Visitors since 1944 (chairman since 1949), on September 19. Mr. Kirchhofer was instrumental in drafting the program to revitalize the leadership at the Institute following Governor Dewey's mandate *for sweeping changes and expanded programs* at the Institute in 1943. We owe a great deal to Mr. Kirchhofer who always worked quietly and efficiently behind the scenes to aid the Institute. While Dr. Wright was interim Institute director, he was able to reassure the staff and provide the confidence it needed.

**9-2.**

BUFFALO NEWS editorial,
"State Commitment
Vital to Roswell
Park Renewal,"
October 10, 1985.

# THE BUFFALO NEWS

Founded October 11, 1880

EDWARD H. BUTLER, Founder 1880-1914    EDWARD H. BUTLER, JR., Publisher 1914-1956

JAMES H. RIGHTER, Publisher 1956-1971    MRS. EDWARD H. BUTLER, Publisher 1971-1974

HENRY Z. URBAN, Publisher 1974-1983

| WARREN E. BUFFETT | STANFORD LIPSEY |
|---|---|
| Chairman | Publisher and President |

Kate Butler Wallis, Vice Chairman; Richard K. Feather, Senior Vice President and Director of Industrial Relations; David W. Perona, Vice President and Circulation Director; Clyde Pinson, Vice President and Advertising Director; Robert L. Moore, Treasurer and Controller; A. Jean Gooding, Secretary and Assistant Treasurer; Albert J. Wainwright, Production Director; Raymond G. Koegel, Inter-Departmental Coordinator

| LEONARD W. HALPERT | MURRAY B. LIGHT | FOSTER L. SPENCER |
|---|---|---|
| Editorial Page Editor | Editor and Senior Vice President | Managing Editor |

Thursday, October 10, 1985        Page B-2

# State Commitment Vital To Roswell Park Renewal

ROSWELL PARK Memorial Institute is one of those entities that not only serve the local community's deepest human needs but also have national importance. State Health Commissioner David Axelrod's renewed pledge of strong commitment to building the strength of the cancer center is a welcome development for both cancer patients and the Buffalo area as a whole — especially since it is backed by some positive suggestions.

Everyone concerned with the well-being of Roswell Park can be glad to see the apparent demise of an earlier state proposal: the idea of moving inpatient beds from the cancer institute to leased space at Buffalo General Hospital. Roswell Park needs to maintain its own physical integrity if it is to be truly successful at its double mission of cancer research and treatment of cancer patients.

Axelrod has now indicated that the Buffalo General option is being dropped in favor of improving the facilities at Roswell Park itself. Whether that eventually means new construction or renovation of present facilities, it is much preferable to splitting off the institute's inpatient beds from the rest of its activities and risking fragmentation and inefficiency.

And while the move might have helped Buffalo General solve its problems of empty beds, other new uses of space at General may in the end provide a much better long-term solution for that institution as well.

One of the most encouraging of Axelrod's remarks in a recent interview was his statement that his department wants Roswell Park to be as comprehensive a cancer center as Sloan-Kettering in New York City, which is now building new patient-care facilities. This kind of commitment indicates a realization among state policy makers that to waste the potential of Roswell Park would be a disservice to the Buffalo area and a much larger surrounding area from which the institute's patients are drawn.

Also encouraging was Axelrod's statement that the state will be looking for "excellence" as it searches for a new permanent director for Roswell Park. Strong, solidly professional leadership will be crucial to the success of the institute in entering what Axelrod himself said will be a "dynamic new era."

The state's new emphasis on a higher level of cooperation between Roswell Park and the State University of Buffalo, with its medical school, is something that should benefit both institutions, and with them, the area of which they are a part.

Roswell Park will need solid guidance if it is to move in the direction of renewal and strengthening Axelrod has outlined. The possible creation of a policy-making board, either independent of the present Board of Visitors or a part of it, deserves serious study by state and local decision makers as they plan the future of the institute.

It looks as if considerable creative thinking about Roswell Park has been going on within the state Health Department. That has to be backed by a commitment that shows itself in the form of funding and positive effort. The community that stands to benefit so greatly now awaits substantive results.

128

Aerial view of the
campus after 1970.

Dr. Hollis Ingraham
in front of mural
of Seventy-fifth
Anniversary with
Congressman
James Hastings.

In 1984 Dr. Murphy
had a private audience
with Pope John Paul II in
Rome. At that occasion,
the Pope extended
a citation to Dr. Murphy
for the Institute's
contributions to cancer
research and treatment
and extended his blessing
to the entire staff.

Dr. Thomas Dougherty
pioneered Photodynamic
Therapy (PDT).

Cancer Information
Service Staff. The Cancer
Information Service
is the oldest service of
its type, initiated by
Dr. Mirand over twenty
years ago. Back Row:
Pat Wolf, Erica Robinson,
Diana Godfrey, Jane
Orlowski, and Bonnie
Woodworth. Middle
Row: Jim Hart, Joanna
Santiano, Susan Harrer,
and Robin Muir. Front
Row: Joanne Janicki,
Sherri Darrow, Ann
Geraci, and Amy Mirand.

Dr. H. James Wallace, Jr., NYS Commissioner of Health Dr. Robert P. Whalen (left), and Miss Patricia Burns tour the Hospital.

Cartoon urging Governor to support Major Modernization Project.

Members of the Roswell Park Alliance meet with Marilyn Quayle upon her visit to Roswell Park in 1991. Dr. Tomasi is present. The Alliance has been very effective in aiding the mission of RPCI in many ways.

More current members of the Roswell Park Alliance.

Architectural rendering
of new Hospital facility
dedicated in May, 1998.
This is part of the $241.5
million Major
Modernization Project.

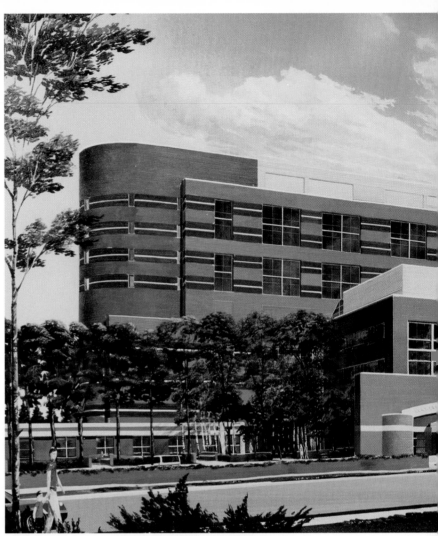

Architectural rendering
of newly constructed
Vivarium and Medical
Research Complex.
This is part of the
$241.5 million Major
Modernization Project.

New Hospital under
construction.

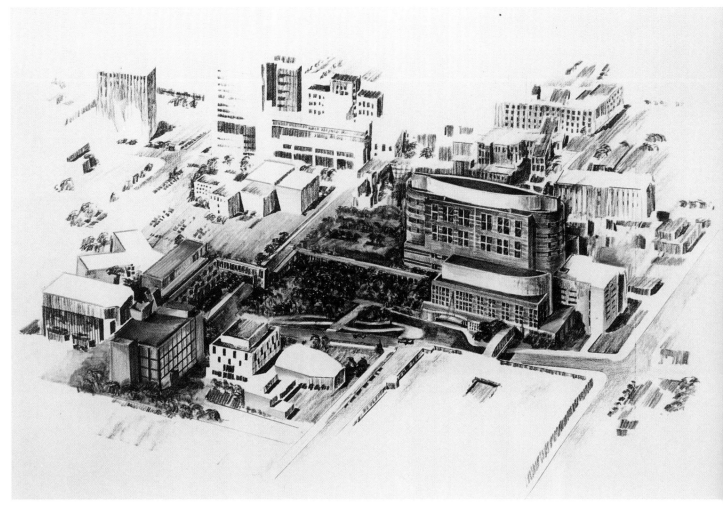

Architectural rendering
of the new campus of
Roswell Park Cancer
Institute when completed
in 1998.

Dr. Thomas B. Tomasi receives an honorary doctorate in science on October 15, 1997, at the occasion of the SUNY at Buffalo Third University Convocation. Left to right: President William Greiner, Dr. Tomasi, former president and CEO, Dr. E. A. Mirand, vice president and dean of RPCI Graduate Division of SUNY at Buffalo.

Dr. Carleton Stewart with technician reviewing flow cytometry data.

Governor George E. Pataki is congratulated after signing RPCI Corporation Bill.

Governor George E. Pataki came to RPCI on October 15, 1997, to sign the bill passed by New York State Assembly and State Senate, to transfer Roswell Park from New York State Department of Health to a Public Benefit Corporation. In the Hilleboe Auditorium in the presence of WNY Legislative Delegation, the Roswell Park Alliance, other community leaders and staff, Governor Pataki said, "our commitment [is] to ensure that Roswell Park remains a leader in cancer research, treatment and education." Dr. David C. Hohn, current President and CEO, is in back right and Governor Pataki is in center back row.

Mrs. Libby Pataki visits the WNY Breast Resource Center at Roswell Park.

The atrium of the new Hospital will feature this sculpture created by Buffalo artist Ellen Steinfeld thanks to generous donation from Irene and Frank Jellinek. The gift was created in memory of Mr. Jellinek's sister and brother-in-law, Louise Jellinek Gross and Max Gross. Steinfeld is an award-winning artist whose works are in many public, corporate and private collections.

**10-1.**
(Left to right) Drs. Edwin
A. Mirand, Thomas B.
Tomasi, and Donald P.
Shedd.

# Chapter 10

# Flexibility and Major Modernization:
## The Tomasi Years

After an intensive national search by the Search Committee headed by Dr. Alfred Gelhorn, director of medical affairs for the New York State Department of Health, Dr. Thomas B. Tomasi, a nationally-known immunologist and former director of the University of New Mexico Cancer Center in Albuquerque, was named president and CEO of Roswell Park June 13, 1986, by State Health Commissioner Dr. David Axelrod. More than thirty people had applied to be successor to Dr. Murphy. Dr. Wright had not declared himself a candidate for the position, nor had he applied.

Dr. Tomasi had discovered the existence of the human mucosal immune system, laying the foundation for the development of oral vaccines, and has been credited with a number of research breakthroughs that furthered the understanding of the role of the immune system in a variety of diseases, including cancer.

In his remarks, Dr. Axelrod commended Dr. John Wright for an *extraordinary job as interim director* and acknowledged the cooperation of Dr. Steven Sample, president, and Dr. John Naughton, dean, of the State University of New York at Buffalo. Dr. Wright resumed his chairmanship of the Department of Pathology at the University at Buffalo and was reappointed to Roswell Park's Board of Visitors by Governor Mario Cuomo.

The administrative core during Dr. Tomasi's tenure was comprised of Dr. Andrew A. Gage, deputy director, Dr. Jerome W. Yates, vice president for Clinical Affairs (Dr. Yates received his post-clinical training at Roswell Park and before returning was successful as head of the Cancer Centers Program at the National Cancer Institute), Dr. Verne M. Chapman, vice president for Research (1985–1989), and Dr. Edwin A. Mirand, vice president for Educational Affairs and dean of the Roswell Park Graduate Division. After Dr. Chapman stepped down in 1989, Dr. James P. Karr served as chief of the Office of Scientific Administration until 1996, when Dr. Youcef Rustum was named vice president for Research. When Dr. Gage retired, Ms. C. Angela Bontempo (former CEO of Sisters of Charity Hospital in Buffalo) was appointed senior vice president and executive director. Dr. Enrico Mihich was appointed vice president for Sponsored Programs and served until 1997. Dr. James P. Nolan joined the administrative staff as special assistant to the president for Outreach and Institutional Affairs. Ms. Dolores Czerwinski, who had been associated with Dr. Tomasi for most of his professional career, served as his devoted administrative assistant and vice president for Community Affairs. Others on Dr. Tomasi's administrative team included: Ms. Catherine A. Lyons, vice president for Nursing; Michael D. DeLellis, director of Operations, Health Research, Inc.; Mr. Arthur DeHey, chief financial officer; Ms. Cindy A. Eller, director of Development; Mrs. Cynthia A. Schwartz, vice president for Governmental Affairs; Mrs. Gail E. Johnstone, director of Planning; Ms. Joyce Buchnowski, director of Public Affairs and Marketing; and Michael J. Quinn, Clinical Practice Plan administrator.

What had been considered unparalleled growth and program expansion under the administrations of Drs. Moore and Murphy took on another significant dimension during the ten-year administration of Dr. Thomas B. Tomasi. Clinical and basic science departments were restructured, new administrative departments were established, senior staff and other faculty members were recruited, new clinical services and programs were developed, new collaborations were established and existing interactions were strengthened, community satellite facilities opened, the campus was reconstructed, and the difficult issue of governance of the Institute was finally addressed to keep pace with changes brought about by managed care.

During the Tomasi administration, Roswell Park reached the threshold of major change to meet the challenges of a changing environment. To carry out the change, Dr. Tomasi restructured the clinical departments within the umbrella divisions of Diagnostic Imaging, Medicine, Pathology, Radiation Medicine, and Surgical Oncology. This configuration allowed for the formation of true multidisciplinary treatment programs and for the streamlining of reporting relationships.

Dr. Tomasi established new clinical services and programs in bone marrow transplantation, pain management, solid tumor oncology, photodynamic therapy, AIDS-related malignancies, plastic and microvascular surgery, brain tumors, orthopedic surgery, cryosurgery, genetic counseling and testing, pigmented lesions, and outpatient chemotherapy. He also established new administrative departments in Public Affairs and Marketing, headed by Mrs. Judi Rice and later by Ms. Joyce Buchnowski; Development, headed by Ms. Cindy A. Eller; and Planning, headed by Mrs. Gail E. Johnstone. The Department of Development has increased private support of Roswell Park twenty-fold since its inception through the energetic and competent efforts of Mrs. Eller and her staff.

This restructuring resulted in eleven new department chiefs, eight senior level scientists, fifteen senior level clinicians, and forty-five additional scientific and medical faculty being recruited. What helped in recruiting prominent clinical staff was the formulation of the first Clinical Practice Plan in the history of the Institute. This effort required bipartisan, statewide legislative support and Governor Mario M. Cuomo's signature on the bill creating the Clinical Practice Plan. This innovative plan long sought after by previous administrations ensured the long-term stability of experienced staff by establishing competitive salaries and enabling physicians, for the first time, to charge for services in the same way as physicians in private practice.

To back up laboratory and clinical research activities, Dr. Tomasi expanded the Institute's shared research resources by adding a biopolymer facility, a cell analysis facility, a chemistry resource laboratory, a flow cytometry facility, a transgenic facility, and a molecular diagnostics facility. He also restructured the protocol office to bring more stringent quality control to bear on the review and monitoring process of clinical studies. Cutting-edge, high-tech equipment was purchased to better serve the needs of patients. The facility expansion was the result of organizing clinical and scientific retreats to help develop long-range plans for the clinical, scientific and educational programs at the Institute.

Dr. Tomasi's efforts extended beyond the bounds of the Institute's campus to garner the support of corporate, civic, and political leadership of the Western New York area. As a result, the Community Council, the Roswell Park Scientific Advisory Council, and the Roswell Park Alliance were formed. Without this effort, Dr. Tomasi's ability to spearhead the $241.5 million Major Modernization Project for a new campus at Roswell Park would have been impossible. (This Project was enacted at a time of fiscal restraint in New York State, and was one of the largest expenditures of its kind ever undertaken by New York State.) In addition, Dr. Tomasi was also able to obtain a National Cancer Institute grant of $500,000 for completion of 9,000 square feet of laboratory space as part of the Major Modernization Project. Under a new dual-level review system, Roswell Park was one of the first three cancer centers in the country to be re-designated by the National Cancer Institute as a Comprehensive Cancer Center.

In conjunction with the City of Buffalo and Buffalo General Hospital (BGH), Dr. Tomasi spearheaded efforts to develop on the Roswell Park campus a hundred-bed "medical inn," costing $10.8 million, to serve patients from BGH and Roswell Park. On July 8, 1997, Dr. R. N. Chopra, president of Med Inn Centers, said the hotel *will help Buffalo become a regional health care center and perhaps a national center eventually.*

Seeing the need to establish new collaborations and strengthen existing interactions with Roswell Park's sister institutions and the State University of New York at Buffalo, Dr. Tomasi initiated the Brain Tumor Treatment Center in conjunction with BGH and Millard Fillmore Hospital and established the Ambulatory Oncology Center, a Roswell Park satellite, at Millard Fillmore Suburban Hospital.

Perhaps Dr. Tomasi's most outstanding achievements during his tenure as president and CEO was working to achieve greater flexibility in the governance of the Institute and obtaining support and funding for the Major Modernization Project.

How *did* Roswell Park finesse $241.5 million from a state notorious for its staggering budget deficits and Gordian knot of bureaucratic red tape? Some would say luck. Most say it was a unique partnership forged by Dr. Tomasi, Governor Cuomo, key legislators, and a community of loyal supporters who refused to abandon an Institute that had helped so many for so long. Among these many supporters was Mr. Peter J. Crotty, Sr., former chairman of the Board of Visitors, who played a major role in getting the attention of Governor Cuomo to aid Roswell Park. Dr. Mirand, a friend of Mr. Crotty's, visited with him in his office and spent the entire afternoon explaining the difficulties that Dr. Tomasi was facing in implementing programs at the Institute. Dr. Mirand suggested that perhaps Mr. Crotty should contact his son, Mr. Gerald C. Crotty, secretary to the Governor, who was then in a position to urge Governor Cuomo to visit the Institute to meet with Dr. Tomasi to discuss the Institute's problems. Mr. Crotty did contact his son and also advised Dr. Mirand to have Dr. Tomasi write a letter to his son Gerald formally inviting the Governor to visit the Institute.

On July 17, 1989, Dr. Tomasi did write to Mr. Gerald Crotty which resulted in Governor Cuomo visiting the Institute August 22, 1989. During this visit, Dr. Tomasi had the opportunity to address the plight of the Institute directly with Governor Cuomo.

Even though the Governor made commitments to the Institute in 1985 and in 1989, it was not until he made another visit to the Institute in 1991, that he said he would do whatever it would take to modernize the Institute. Governor Cuomo's pronouncement, *I am committed, WATCH!* (which he also wrote in the Institute Guest Book) became the banner phrase for efforts to push the Major Modernization Project of Roswell Park forward. Even the Governor feared that his words—one of the boldest commitments he had ever made to a single state facility—would come back to haunt him, he said, *There were times I wished I hadn't put that promise in writing in your Guest Book.*

**10-2.**
RPCI Family Portrait
presented to Governor
Cuomo when he signed
Flexibility Legislation
Bill on August 11, 1992.

The cornerstone of the Major Modernization had been symbolically laid in 1986 when Dr. David Axelrod, former commissioner of the NYS Department of Health, charged Tomasi with the revitalization of the Buffalo-based cancer center. *I believed then as I believe now that the Modernization of Roswell Park would not rest on the mixing of mortar and the strategic placement of bricks,* Tomasi noted. *We needed leadership, staff, equipment, support. We weren't just another hospital requiring a facelift. We had a history and reputation to live up to.*

Tomasi soon learned that the prescription for change would not come easily for he was confronted with the mindset that "less is better" by some Albany officials. *Whoever said less is more wasn't running a comprehensive cancer center,* Tomasi said. *Limited resources became a euphemism for make do. Each morning, I'd wonder what new challenge we'd be facing that day.*

One of Tomasi's most politically strategic moves, for assistance in reinforcing the Governor's original commitment, was to organize the Community Council, an advisory group of prominent business leaders and educators whose legislative and community influence was undeniable. The Community Council was headed by Mr. David Campbell and later by Mr. Robert G. Wilmers, with R. O. Anderson, Anne Gioia, Anthony Gioia, Jean Knox, Gerald S. Lippes, Alfred Price, Dr. Andrew Rudnick, and Dr. John R. Wright. Another move was to reacquaint the Western New York Delegation (comprised of senators and assemblymen from the eight counties in Western New York) with the Institute through meetings with staff and tours of the Institute. A steady stream of information flowed from Buffalo to Albany and back again. The Roswell Park Alliance, a community-wide volunteer organization of civic and social leaders, was formed. This group initiated important programs for patients, sponsored major fund-raising events, and raised community awareness. Collectively, the three groups served as a magnet to coalesce community and political support for the Institute. *These individuals were phenomenal,* said Tomasi. *They worked non-stop, calling in favors, applying pressure, getting our message out.*

In 1989 Dr. Tomasi realized his dream for the Major Modernization Project had to be properly outlined and began to formulate the project with the selection of a team of architects, planners, engineers, and market and financial analysts headed by Bohm NBBJ to conduct the planning project. An interagency core committee of key management from Roswell Park headed by hard-working Director of Planning Gail Johnstone, assisted by Mr. William Clark and Mrs. Cynthia Schwartz, the New York State Department of Health, Office of General Services, and the Dormitory Authority set out to prepare a Major Modernization Project proposal that would be reviewed and approved by each agency represented on the core committee.

The Major Modernization Project proposal called for the construction of a new Diagnostic and Treatment Center for radiation therapy, diagnostic imaging, nuclear medicine, and surgery with its related postanesthesia care unit, intensive care unit, and central sterile supply. *These services,* said Tomasi, *are at the core of treatment for virtually every patient at the Institute and have a direct, major impact on revenue generation and operating efficiency.* The Major Modernization Project proposal demonstrated that construction of the Center could begin in 1993. A new Medical Research Complex would be entirely completed by the year 2000. The new laboratory facility would include a new vivarium which will centralize disparate animal facilities presently spread over five buildings on campus and two off campus. The plan also called for the renovation of other laboratory space to remediate obsolete mechanical and electrical systems and to provide additional space to meet the needs of Roswell Park's strong basic science programs. Other priorities include the construction of a pedestrian walkway system to unite the campus, replacement/modernization of inpatient beds, and expansion of outpatient facilities, correction of life safety, health code, and infrastructure deficiencies, and restoration of structured parking.

The impact of the Major Modernization Project obviously would extend beyond Western New York to the state and nation. In addition to enhancing Roswell Park's national presence in the cancer effort, the project, it was felt, should increase inpatient and outpatient activity, provide a larger employment base, create a more competitive research environment with increased grants, establish unique, specialized patient services, widen the patient referral base, and ensure economic development leverage for Buffalo and Western New York.

What became a Major Modernization Project Proposal began to be fulfilled by March 1992. Governor Cuomo's promise to rebuild Roswell's campus through a bond authorization for $241.5 became a reality, when both the Assembly and Senate voted on the same day to approve the measure. The Major Modernization Project became the largest health-related project ever approved by New York State and the only health-related project approved for the State's fiscal year 1992. Also, the New York State legislature voted to officially change the name of Roswell Park Memorial Institute to Roswell Park Cancer Institute to better reflect its mission. Dr. Tomasi called the passage of the bill a *resounding confirmation of the facility's importance to the State and the most significant step forward in the history of the Institute.*

On August 11, 1992, Roswell Park staff, patients, visitors, and state and local dignitaries stood and applauded as Governor Cuomo entered the Institute's packed Hilleboe Auditorium for the formal bill signing ceremony. Dr. Tomasi related, *This provided relief because we had won a long, hard fight. Elation because we had taken a giant step toward accomplishing what we had set out to do and gratitude to the many individuals whose response to* it can't be done *was always* it will be done.

**10-3.**

BUFFALO NEWS editorial,
"A New Day for Roswell
Park as State Keeps Its
Promise," June 28, 1992.

# A new day for Roswell Park as state keeps its promise

## $241 million is badge of real commitment

MAYBE SEEING is believing. After holding its collective breath while a succession of state leaders came for themselves to see the demise — and the potential — of Roswell Park Cancer Institute, the area can exhale with the State Legislature's approval of $241 million to modernize the aging facility.

It seems Albany's key players now believe what this area long knew: Roswell Park is too valuable to squander through physical neglect and fiscal myopia.

Gov. Cuomo and Lt. Gov. Lundine deserve credit for putting the issue on the Albany agenda with a proposal to bond the work. Each toured the facility in the past year and found it lacking, a result of long-term state neglect.

But the state's legislative leaders also merit credit. Senate Majority Leader Ralph Marino and Assembly Speaker Saul Weprin also made the trek here last year, thanks to persistent lobbying by this area's own delegation of state legislators. Both the Legislature leaders vowed to help.

Still, the promises of politicians sometimes draw deserved skepticism, particularly in a period of tight budgets when money to pay off debt will be tough to come by. Not so in this case, as the Legislature approved the money that will allow both structural and staffing improvements at this nationally significant cancer center.

Most apparent to the public will be the physical facelift that will include a new diagnostic and treatment center, as well as new clinics and repairs to existing facilities. All of it is a belated effort to restore Roswell Park as a place of international prominence as a cancer research and treatment center.

But while the new facilities will attract the most attention, budgetary changes that will untie the center's hands may have the greatest long-term significance.

Restrictions on hiring and adequately paying staff were a direct result of the state's recent budget crises. Their impact has been devastating on Roswell Park. The facility has been unable to attract or retain doctors with the prominence a facility like this one should command.

The legislation helps correct for that with a new billing arrangement that will help the facility compete for top doctors. They, in turn, will draw more patients and research money.

While doing all of that, the legislation also officially changes the facility's name from Roswell Park Memorial Institute to Roswell Park Cancer Institute, to better reflect its mission.

But the most significant change may well be the one in the state's attitude toward this invaluable facility.

Roswell Park is too important to be sacrificed as part of the annual budget battle. This legislation — belatedly, but correctly — recognizes that fact.

To return to major senior staff appointments during Dr. Tomasi's administration, Dr. Clara Bloomfield was selected to chair the newly established Division of Medicine, with leadership responsibilities for the departments of Solid Tumor Oncology/Investigational Therapeutics and Hematologic Oncology/Bone Marrow Transplantation. She was also appointed chief of Medical Oncology at SUNY at Buffalo, with administrative responsibility for training and research programs at University-affiliated teaching hospitals.

After an intensive national search, Ms. Catherine A. Lyons, RN, MS, was appointed director of Nursing, succeeding Georgia M. Burnette, RN, MS. Dr. Kenneth A. Foon was appointed chief of the newly established Department of Clinical Immunology, and Dr. Mark A. Lema, a Ph.D. graduate of the Roswell Park Graduate Division and anesthesiologist at Brigham & Women's Hospital of Harvard Medical School, was appointed chief of the Department of Anesthesiology. Mrs. Cindy A. Eller was appointed to head the Institute's first Department of Development which administered programs for annual memorial and special gifts as well as to write grant applications to private foundations for support of non-research and capital areas.

Dr. Carleton Stewart, a noted immunologist from Los Alamos National Laboratory and one of the world's authorities on flow cytometry, joined the staff in 1988. Dr. Steven J. Greenberg, an alumni of Roswell Park's summer training program, returned to chair the newly formed Department of Neurology. Dr. Nicholas J. Petrelli was appointed chairman of the newly formed Division of Surgical Oncology, which includes the departments of Breast Surgery, Head & Neck/Section of Plastic & Reconstructive Surgery, Lower Gastrointestinal, Soft Tissue/Melanoma and Bone, Thoracic Surgery and Upper Gastrointestinal/Endoscopy.

**10-4.**
Governor Mario M. Cuomo signing Major Modernization Project with WNY State legislators witnessing on August 11, 1992.

**10-5.**
Governor Cuomo with NYS Commissioner of Health Dr. Mark Chassin, Dr. Tomasi, and Mr. David Campbell at the time of the signing of the legislation of flexibility and modernization on August 11, 1992. (Left to right: Dr. Chassin, Governor Cuomo, Dr. Tomasi, and David Campbell).

**10-6.**
Governor Cuomo with left to right: Dr. Tomasi, Daniel Brody, Senator Anthony Masiello, Assemblyman Arthur Eve, Governor Cuomo, Senator Dale Volker, and Assemblyman Robin Schimminger at the time of the signing of the bill of flexibility and modernization on August 11, 1992.

**10-7.**
Mrs. Anne Gioia, chair of Roswell Park Alliance who played a significant role in legislation at August 11, 1992, signing being interviewed by Channel 7.

**10-8.**
David Campbell holding up certificate in grateful recognition of his efforts in helping to obtain flexibility and modern-ization legislation on August 11, 1992. On his right is Assemblyman Paul Tokasz.

**10-9.**
Left to right: Mrs. Pamela Jacobs from Roswell Park Alliance, Mr. J. Campbell, OHSA, Commissioner of Health Dr. Mark Chassin, and Dr. Enrico Mihich at legislation signing on August 11, 1992.

**10-10.**
Left to right: Vice President for Health Affairs and Dean of Medical School Dr. John Naughton and Mr. David Campbell with Dr. Andrew Gage at the time of the legislation signing on August 11, 1992.

**10-11.**
BUFFALO NEWS article on Roswell Park receiving $241.5 million from New York State. Left to right: Mr. Gerald S. Lippes and Mrs. Donna Gioia who aided the effort.

Roswell Park's state-of-the-art bone marrow transplantation program reopened under the leadership of Dr. Geoffrey Herzig, who has been credited with reporting the nation's best long-term survival rates for leukemia patients undergoing transplants. Dr. Derek Raghavan, a top cancer specialist from Australia, was appointed chief of the Department of Solid Tumor Oncology/Investigational Therapeutics. Dr. John S. J. Brooks, from the Hospital and School of Medicine of the University of Pennsylvania, was appointed chairman of the Division of Pathology. Dr. Paul C. Stomper became director of the Mammography Center. He published a critically-acclaimed Cancer Imaging Manual, the first text to describe and illustrate criteria selection, technique and interpretation of anatomical and functional imaging tests for various diagnostic evaluations. Dr. Martin L. Brecher was appointed chief of Pediatrics, carrying on the fine tradition of the Department of Pediatrics founded by Dr. Donald Pinkel in 1956, and later headed by Dr. Jean Cortner, Dr. Lucius Sinks and Dr. Arnold Freeman.

Two new clinical services were added at this time—a Lymphedema Treatment Service and a Satellite Unit of Hospice Buffalo, under the direction of Dr. Stephen B. Edge. Dr. William G. Kraybill was appointed chief of the Department of Soft Tissue Sarcoma/Melanoma/Bone in the Division of Surgical Oncology. Dr. Robert A. Fenstermaker, a neurosurgical oncologist from Case Western Reserve, joined the staff of the Department of Neurosurgery. Dr. Mark A. Delacure was appointed chief of the Department of Head & Neck/Section of Plastic & Reconstructive Surgery, Division of Surgical Oncology, following the retirement of Dr. Donald P. Shedd.

Other appointments included: Dr. Allan R. Oseroff, chief of the Department of Dermatology; Dr. Kyu Shin, chairman of the Division of Radiation Medicine; Dr. Emerson Colby, chairman of the Department of Laboratory Animal Resources; and Maureen Hammond, CSW, director of Social Work.

Dr. Walter T. Murphy, chief of radiation therapy at Roswell Park from 1939 to 1963, died October 14, 1989. Dr. Walter Murphy was the author of the now-classic 1,041-page textbook RADIATION THERAPY, which was praised by the JOURNAL OF THE AMERICAN MEDICAL ASSOCIATION as *a monumental piece of work.* Dr. Joseph E. Sokal, chief of Medicine, Section B, from 1955 to 1979, died on October 12, 1989. During his career, Dr. Sokal was active as a researcher, clinician and educator, who helped to establish Roswell Park as a leader in research and treatment, particularly on myelogenous leukemia.

Dr. David Harker, founding father of modern crystallography and former director of the Department of Biophysics and Center for Crystallographic Research, died February 27, 1991, at the age of eighty-four. Harker's scientific breakthroughs contributed directly to contemporary knowledge of the molecular structure of drugs, hormones, proteins, and antibiotics and the molecular basis for chemical and biological processes. *He was one of the greatest crystallographers of this century . . . a tireless seeker of truth, wherever he could find it, and in his quest he succeeded as few others have,* said Nobel Laureate Dr. Herbert Hauptman.

**10-15.**
Director of Nursing
Catherine Lyons shows
members of Roswell
Park Alliance through
the Bone Marrow
Transplant Unit.

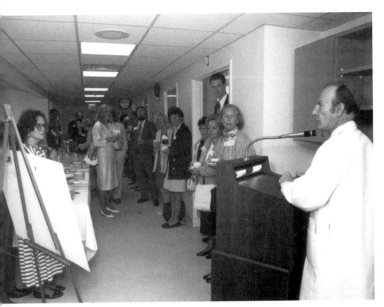

**10-14.**
Dr. T. Tomasi reopening
the Bone Marrow
Transplant Unit.

Dr. Charles R. West, chief of the Department of Neurosurgery for twenty-two years, died December 6, 1996. Dr. West was an early proponent of tapping the expertise and resources of medicine, surgery, and radiotherapy to create comprehensive, multidisciplinary treatments for brain and spinal cord tumor patients. His commitment to developing more effective drugs for brain tumor led to his receiving four U.S. patents.

While the way the Institute did business was changing in a managed care environment, the mission to find the causes and cures for cancer remained constant. The quality of research and patient care remained high. Some of the achievements and special recognition of the Roswell Park staff during Dr. Tomasi's administration are included in the following paragraphs.

A unique case report of a Roswell Park patient published in 1986 became the key which opened the field of genetic research of cancer. Dr. Lemuel Herrera and associates from the Department of Surgery published a case report of a mentally retarded patient with colon cancer, familial adenomatous polyposis, and other chromosomal anomalies. At the time of the report, there had been only five cases of abnormalities on chromosome 5 reported in the literature, with Roswell Park being the first and only research institute to describe a constitutional chromosome anomaly in a patient with Gardner's syndrome and colorectal cancer. Despite several years of intensive research, this was the first time that a cytogenetic finding led to the discovery of a recessive genetic effect in one of the most common types of cancer. (This research triggered both the 1987 breakthrough genetic study by British scientists who located the genetic defect responsible for Familial Adenomatous Polyposis (FAP) on the long arm of chromosome 5; and the December 2, 1993, announcement by the National Center for Human Genome Research that the gene for colon cancer had been identified.)

Roswell Park was designated one of eleven centers in North America to participate in one of the largest antismoking studies ever funded by the National Cancer Institute. The goal of Roswell Park's portion of the eight-year community intervention trial (COMMIT) was to determine if a community-based antismoking campaign could significantly decrease cigarette smoking. The $2.2 million study, under the direction of Dr. K. Michael Cummings, involved the cities of Utica and Binghamton in New York State.

Dr. K. Michael Cummings and Russell Sciandra, director of the Cancer Information Service, co-authored a section of the U.S. Surgeon General's Twenty-fifth Anniversary Report on Smoking and Health. Their section, "Smoking Education and Cessation Activities," reviewed the public education and smoking cessation activities of groups and organizations that comprise the smoking control movement in the United States over the past twenty-five years.

The CAN-DIAL number, 1-800-462-1884, was selected by the New York State Department of Health as a statewide resource for referrals to low-cost mammography. City, county, and state officials and leaders joined Roswell Park in unveiling its Health Express mobile cancer education center on April 7, 1988, as part of the New York State Department of Health effort to bring breast cancer education and services to minority and medically underserved women. Dr. Curtis J. Mettlin, director of the Department of Cancer Control and Epidemiology, joined leaders of the American Cancer Society (ACS) at a White House meeting to present the ACS report to the nations on "Cancer and the Poor" to the President. The report was based on a series of regional meetings held by the ACS National Committee on Socioeconomically Disadvantaged, chaired by Dr. Mettlin, in collaboration with the Centers for Disease Control and the National Cancer Institute.

Dr. Andrew A. Gage, deputy director, received an honorary award from the American Society for Contemporary Medicine and Surgery for his pioneering role in developing the implantable cardiac pacemaker.

Dr. Carl Porter, a researcher in the Department of Experimental Therapeutics, made a key discovery in 1987 when he found a link between polyamines, a chemical substance found in high concentrations in human semen, and the development and growth of certain types of cancer. Dr. Porter headed a national program to investigate the role polyamines play in proliferation of cancer cells and their potential as target sites for cancer chemotherapy.

Successes in lung cancer vaccine trials, involving specific tumor-associated antigen conducted and reported by researchers from George Washington University, Roswell Park, Ottawa University and Allegheny General Hospital in 1987, raised hopes for the future of immunotherapy. Five-year survival rates in 234 lung cancer patients who participated in the trials showed a 20 percent survival advantage for vaccinated patients over controls.

The Division of Medicine was invited to participate in its first chemoprevention trial as part of the National Cancer Institute's burgeoning efforts to develop drugs to prevent or arrest cancer development.

Georgia M. Burnette, director of Nursing, was elected president of the Professional Nurses Association of Western New York District I, New York State Nurses Association, Inc. Dr. Enrico Mihich was installed as president of the AACR; the tenth member of the Roswell Park staff to serve as president of this prestigious organization.

The Twenty-eighth Annual Meeting of the Association for Gnotobiotics, held in Buffalo, was dedicated to Dr. Edwin A. Mirand for his contributions to the field. Dr. Mirand was president of the association in 1968 and served on the Board of Directors from 1967 to 1970 and from 1975 to 1978. He also was the president of the International Association for Gnotobiology from 1981 to 1984.

Roswell Park hosted two international meetings: the International Conference on Complications of Treatment of Children and Adolescents for Cancer and the Third Biennial Meeting of the International Photodynamic Association. Dr. Daniel M. Green served as program chairman for the former, and Dr. Thomas J. Dougherty, who pioneered PDT, and Dr. Barbara Henderson co-chaired the conference.

The national spotlight focused on Dr. M. Steven Piver and the Institute in 1990. Crews from three national television programs interviewed Dr. Piver on ovarian cancer and the Familial Ovarian Cancer Registry, headquartered at Roswell Park. In less than one month, Dr. Piver was interviewed for segments on *Face-to-Face* with Connie Chung, CBS, and *20/20* and *Nightline* on ABC. Dr. Piver later appeared on the *Oprah Winfrey Show*, *Good Morning America* and many other national network productions.

Dermatologists at Roswell Park began using photophoresis to treat cutaneous T-cell lymphoma. Roswell Park was one of the few facilities offering this safe, effective procedure which has now been approved by the Food and Drug Administration as a standard treatment for advanced stages of this disease.

The Department of Dermatology was awarded a $500,000 grant from the National Cancer Institute to test isotretinoin, a vitamin-A derivative, as a way to prevent skin cancer. Roswell Park was one of only eight centers selected to participate in the national study.

The Division of Radiation Medicine successfully performed Western New York's first stereotactic surgery on a patient with a recurrent malignant brain tumor.

The Division of Radiation Medicine successfully treated its first patient with high-dose brachytherapy, a rapid, more efficient way of delivering high doses of radiation directly to tumors. Roswell Park participated in the National Cancer Institute's tamoxifen trial, the largest breast cancer prevention study ever undertaken in the United States. A Nicotine Dependence Clinic, which targets heavy smokers, was added to the Institute's Smoking Control Program. This program was one of the first in the nation to offer the nicotine patch as a smoking cessation aid.

A Roswell Park study showed that smoking-related illnesses cost New York State $4 billion annually. As a result, antismoking lobbyists called for a doubling of the State's cigarette tax.

Roswell Park released the results of its study on the health effects of environmental tobacco smoke shortly before legislative approval June 15 of New York State's Clean Indoor Air Act. The act, which was introduced by Senate Health Committee Chairman Michael Tully, provides protection for nonsmokers in public places, restaurants, and the workplace. Senator Tully cited the Roswell Park study in statements urging passage of his bill.

Dr. Daniel M. Green, Department of Pediatrics, was unanimously elected chairperson of the National Wilms' Tumor Study Committee. Dr. Clara D. Bloomfield was elected to the Board of Directors of the American Society of Clinical Oncology.

The GOOD HOUSEKEEPING's list of the "Best Cancer Doctors in America" included five physicians from Roswell Park: Dr. Harold O. Douglass, Jr. (gastrointestinal cancer), Dr. M. Steven Piver (gynecologic cancer), Dr. Clara Bloomfield and Dr. Geoffrey Herzig (leukemia), and Dr. Constantine Karakousis (melanoma).

Roswell Park hosted the annual meeting of the Association of American Cancer Institutes, June 23–24, 1992. Dr. Edwin Mirand, secretary-treasurer of the group, welcomed more than a hundred cancer center directors from North America. The Second International Conference on the Long-Term Complications of Treatment of Children and Adolescents for Cancer was again hosted by the Institute.

In 1993 researchers from the Department of Molecular Immunology reported arresting the growth of human lung tumor xenograft in severe immunodeficient (SCID) mice by administering a long-circulating liposome formation of the drug doxorubicin. This was the first direct evidence that anticancer drugs delivered in this way are more effective in halting the growth of human tumors than more conventional delivery systems. This was well received.

Roswell Park was named one of the nation's ten best cancer hospitals in an annual guide to America's best hospitals published in 1993 by U.S. NEWS & WORLD REPORT.

The Family Cancer Syndrome Registry was established by the Division of Surgical Oncology to track families that carry the gene for hereditary nonpolyposis colon cancer. The well-regarded registry identifies families in which at least three members within two generations have had colorectal cancer, with one member diagnosed before the age of fifty.

Dr. Steven J. Greenberg, chairman of the Department of Neurology, co-edited PCR-BASED DIAGNOSTICS IN INFECTIOUS DISEASES, the first comprehensive collection of polymerase chain reaction-based diagnostic methodologies for the detection of microbial infections.

Dr. T. Ming Chu received two prestigious awards in 1993 for his pioneering research on prostate-specific antigen and the development of the PSA test. The Presidential Citation Award was presented jointly by the American Urological Association and the American Foundation for Urological Disease *to individuals deemed to have significantly promoted urology's cause during a specific period of time.* The Dornier Innovative Research Award of the American Foundation for Urological Disease recognizes *individuals who best exemplify the spirit of imagination and inquiry driving the research objectives of the Foundation.*

In 1994 Senator Robert Dole (R-Kansas), who waged a personal campaign to increase public awareness of prostate cancer, accepted the Gilda Radner Courage Award from the Roswell Park Alliance at the Alliance black-tie fund-raiser. Dole, who credits the PSA test with saving his life through early detection, received the Award from PSA pioneer and Roswell researcher Dr. T. Ming Chu. *I look forward to shaking the hand of the man responsible for the PSA test,* said the senator before meeting Dr. Chu.

A team of international researchers, including members of Roswell Park's Division of Medicine, reported in a pioneering study published in NATURE, 1994, that they have identified the unique cells that cause acute myeloid leukemia. This discovery may one day lead to the development of more effective strategies to treat this common form of adult leukemia.

DNA samples from families registered in the Gilda Radner Ovarian Cancer Registry were used for research on the BRCA1 gene—the gene linked to familial breast cancer and ovarian cancer. Dr. M. Steven Piver, chairman of the Department of Gynecologic Oncology, co-authored the first paper documenting a link to BRCA1 in families with hereditary ovarian cancer in which there were three or more close relatives with ovarian cancer, but no cases of breast cancer in these families before the age of fifty.

Roswell Park was again listed among the nation's five best cancer hospitals in an annual guide to America's best hospitals published by U.S. NEWS & WORLD REPORT. In addition, five Roswell Park faculty members—Drs. Patrick Creaven (Medicine), Daniel Green (Pediatrics), Geoffrey Herzig (Medicine), Derek Raghavan (Medicine), and Clara Bloomfield (Medicine) were cited in THE BEST DOCTORS IN AMERICA, a directory of the *best and brightest* in the medical profession published by Woodward-White.

Roswell Park was invited to participate in the National Cancer Institute-sponsored Prostate Cancer Prevention Trial to test the effectiveness of the drug finasteride in preventing prostate cancer. Eighteen thousand men at 222 sites throughout the United States are expected to enroll.

Roswell Park was one of the first cancer institutes to have a regional Cancer Information Service and, in 1994, the National Cancer Institute awarded to Dr. E. A. Mirand a $4 million, five-year contract to the Cancer Information Service at Roswell Park. The new contract expanded the service area to include most of New York (excluding New York City, Long Island, and Westchester County) and the twenty-nine counties in Western Pennsylvania.

Roswell Park staff members continued to be recognized for their work. Dr. Stephen Edge, chief of Breast Surgery, was the only Western New York representative appointed to a New York State panel of healthcare experts and consumers assembled to evaluate breast cancer treatment in New York State.

Dr. William Carl, Department of Dentistry and Maxillofacial Prosthetics, received the International Service Award from the American Dental Association for the third time in his career for his work with residents in remote areas of Kenya. He previously received the award for his clinical work in Haiti, Honduras, and Sierra Leone.

The Institute for Advanced Studies in Immunology and Aging presented its Lifetime Service Award to Dr. Enrico Mihich, chair of the Department of Experimental Therapeutics, at the Fourth Symposium on Combination Therapies, held in Sardinia, Italy. Mihich was honored for *contributions to the field of experimental therapeutics, particularly for his groundbreaking work on biological response modifiers.*

In 1995 local experts pointed to Roswell Park as Western New York's best hope and opportunity for regional economic stability and expansion. Roswell Park continued to hold its own in grants, patents, biotechnology transfers, and partnerships. Within the year, Roswell Park investigators were awarded $32.7 million in research support, including $26.9 million in federal grants and contracts; $1.6 million in commercial sponsorships and $4.2 million in royalties and donations. Roswell Park maintained research and development clinical trials with twenty-five private biopharmaceutical corporations, and held forty-six licenses and thirty-two patents.

Roswell Park researchers discovered fibers of cigarette filters in the cancerous lungs of smokers, suggesting that filters may actually contribute to, rather than prevent, the development of lung disease and cancer. Dr. John L. Pauly, of the Department of Molecular Immunology, and his colleagues reported that there is probable cause to suggest that cellulose acetate filter fibers are inhaled or ingested, and may become lodged indefinitely in the lung tissue of longtime smokers.

Also in the Department of Molecular Immunology, researchers were cited for exploring the seemingly unlimited possibilities of delivering effective vaccines for Hepatitis-B virus, the leading cause of liver cancer, in genetically-engineered foods. Dr. Yasmin Thanavala determined that genetically-engineered foods, such as bananas and potatoes, may replace traditional fermentation systems to produce vaccines.

In the the Department of Molecular Immunology, Dr. Richard Bankert was using a mouse model (SCID) to show for the first time that it is possible to evaluate human immunologically-based therapies in vivo, before resorting to human clinical trials. Dr. Elizabeth Repasky has shown that cell adhesion is the key element in normal immune function which apparently requires a dynamic reorganization of cytoskeletal proteins.

In the Department of Human Genetics, Drs. Pieter deJong, Thomas Shows, and John Yates were recognized for their studies on isolating, characterizing, and understanding oncogenes and DNA sequences associated with cancer. Likewise, Drs. Lynne Maquat and Alan Kinniburgh were cited for research directed at understanding how gene expression is genetically controlled.

Research projects in other research departments which were well received included: Dr. Joel Huberman on the mechanism of control of the cell cycle; Dr. William Burhans on initiation of DNA replication; Drs. Rosemary Elliott, Richard Swank, and Kenneth Manly on gene mapping; Dr. Edward Morgan on gene regulation and structure: Dr. Kenneth Gross on regulation of genes in specific tissues; Dr. Steven Pruitt and Dr. Paul D. Soloway on the regulation of gene development; Dr. John Subjeck on cellular responses to stresses and physiological signals, such as heat shock, anoxia; Dr. Heinz Bauman on inflammatory cytokines; and Drs. Bonnie and Harold Asch on identifying and characterizing factors and events that drive the progression of normal mammary epithelium to malignancy.

Dr. Margot Ip, of the Department of Experimental Therapeutics, was invited to serve as a member of the Chemical Pathology Study Section, Division of Research Grants, of the National Institutes of Health. Dr. Ip's selection was based on her scientific stature, contributions to the fields of cell biology and endocrine oncology, and the quality of her research. Others in the Department of Experimental Therapeutics—Drs. H. L. Gurtoo, B. J. Dolnick, M. V. Bobek, P. W. Kanter, and J. J. McGuire—have been recognized as well.

Drs. W. R. Greco and L. E. Blumenson from the Biomathematics Resource Facility designed a computer program which accurately and objectively records and analyzes data for tumor growth.

Roswell Park was rated one of the top medical facilities in the United States and Canada, according to the BEST HOSPITALS IN AMERICA, a comprehensive guide to the services offered by the most prestigious medical institutions in North America. PREVENTION MAGAZINE'S "Guide to Health: For Men Only" listed Roswell Park as one of the nation's three best facilities for cancer treatment. Memorial Sloan-Kettering Cancer Center and M.D. Anderson Center were also cited.

The United States Food and Drug Administration approved the drug Photofrin—developed by Dr. Thomas Dougherty of Roswell Park—as a palliative treatment for patients with obstructing esophageal cancers. This was the first photodynamic therapy drug to be approved in the United States. One of the country's largest mesothelioma studies was initiated by the Department of Thoracic Surgery to determine if photodynamic therapy has an impact on patient prognosis.

A medical team of physicians, radiologists, and nurses offered cryosurgery, a surgical procedure which uses liquid nitrogen to freeze tumors, to prostate cancer patients who were unable to tolerate conventional therapy. Roswell Park was the only hospital in Buffalo to offer this treatment.

Dr. Norman G. Schaaf, chair of Dentistry and Maxillofacial Prosthetics, received the Andrew J. Ackerman Award from the American Academy of Maxillofacial Prosthetics for outstanding contributions to maxillofacial prosthetics. This award is not given annually and is reserved by the Academy to honor only outstanding professionals.

Dr. Thomas B. Tomasi was named 1995 Renaissance Man by the Buffalo Renaissance Foundation, a civic and philanthropic group of young businessmen dedicated to building a better Buffalo. Dr. Tomasi was later awarded the George F. Koepf, MD Award from the Hauptman-Woodward Medical Research Institute, Inc., for his contributions to the advancement of biomedical research.

The results of a landmark study by Drs. Garth Anderson, Department of Molecular and Cellular Biology, and Morton S. Kahlenberg, Division of Surgical Oncology, which cast doubt on the widely held belief that the mutation of the p53 gene triggers the chain reaction of cancer development, were published in the November 20, 1995, issue of the JOURNAL OF THE NATIONAL CANCER INSTITUTE. This research broke faith with dogma long held by the scientific community regarding the role of the p53 gene and cancer tumors. Conventional wisdom had held that the p53 gene played the central role when gene systems ran amok.

Dr. Enrico Mihich, director of the Department of Experimental Therapeutics, was invited to serve on the Board of Scientific Advisors of the National Cancer Institute, which assists and advises the NCI director on all aspects of the group's extramural program. In addition, the Board is responsible for advising extramural division directors on scientific policies, both present and future, and for concept review of research and resource activities. Dr. Mihich also received an honorary doctor of medicine from the University of Marseilles, France.

The International Society for Oncodevelopmental Biology and Medicine presented its 1996 Abbott Award to Dr. T. Ming Chu, director of the Department of Diagnostic Immunology, in recognition of his pioneering work on prostate-specific antigen (PSA) and the development of the PSA test for prostate cancer.

There were a number of developments in the Division of Surgical Oncology headed by Dr. Nicholas J. Petrelli in 1996. A Clinical Genetics Service, one of the first at a comprehensive cancer center, was established to provide women at high-risk for breast cancer with counseling, instruction, and gene testing, if desired. Under a clinical research protocol, the BRCA1 test is available to women who have been diagnosed with breast cancer and have a family history of breast and/or ovarian cancer, or are a relative of a BRCA1 carrier.

The Cancer Information Service celebrated its twentieth anniversary this year. Cited by the National Cancer Advisory Board as the oldest, largest, and most successful cancer communications program in the country, the CIS at Roswell Park responds to 20,000 lengthy telephone calls annually.

In its March issue, AMERICAN HEALTH magazine cites three Roswell Park clinicians as being among America's 1,000 best doctors: Dr. Nicholas Petrelli (in Surgical Oncology), Dr. Geoffrey Herzig (in Hematology/Oncology), and Dr. Derek Raghavan (in Medical Oncology). The magazine later cited Surgical Oncology and Breast Surgery as being the best in the nation.

Fifteen specialists from Roswell Park appear in the 1996–1997 edition of THE BEST DOCTORS IN AMERICA, NORTHEAST REGION, published by Woodward/White, Inc. Specialists named are Drs. Peter Aplan (Pediatric Hematology/Oncology); Clara Bloomfield (Leukemias/Lymphomas); Martin Brecher (Pediatric Hematology/Oncology); Patrick Creaven (Clinical Pharmacology); Geoffrey Herzig (Bone Marrow Transplantation; Leukemias/Lymphomas); Daniel Green (Pediatric Hematology/Oncology); Steven Greenberg (Neurology); Wesley L. Hicks (General Surgical Oncology); Robert Huben (Urologic Oncology); Ellis Levine (Breast Cancer); M. Steven Piver (Gynecologic Oncology); Derek Raghavan (Genitourinary Cancer; Lung Cancer; Solid Tumors); Donald P. Shedd (General Surgical Oncology); Paul Stomper (Radiology); and Hiroshi Takita (Surgical Oncology).

Researchers in the Division of Medicine were selected to test a promising new vaccine against pancreatic cancer, a silent, virulent disease which boasts one of cancer's poorest survival rates.

The Department of Experimental Therapeutics celebrated its Fortieth Anniversary with a symposium on "Molecular Approaches to Cancer Therapeutics" which featured presentations by former graduate students who graduated from the Roswell Park Graduate Division

Modification to existing facilities were required from time to time to implement programs. Dr. Tomasi responded as well as he could to meet the requests of the staff. These requests for additions or alterations reflect program needs in laboratory and clinical research and education. During this period, the Institute's equipment for patient care and research had increased as programs expanded and became updated through the addition of newly developed instruments. Among the facilities added during this time are as follows.

Roswell Park opened a Long-Term Follow-up Clinic—the first of its type in the United States— to provide specialized medical care, support and counseling to long-term survivors of childhood cancer, under the direction of Dr. Daniel Green, cancer research pediatrician.

The departments of Nursing and Anesthesiology opened the Progressive Care Unit, a facility designed to accommodate patients who require specialized monitoring or observation, but are not candidates for the intensive care unit or general nursing care unit.

To help open the Institute's new state-of-the-art Mammography Center, directed by Dr. Paul Stomper, Matilda Cuomo, wife of Governor Mario Cuomo, visited Roswell Park to introduce a new public service campaign designed to raise awareness of the importance of mammography in the early detection of breast cancer.

Dr. Tomasi moved forward with plans to continue the revitalization of the Institute. Several inpatient units and laboratories were renovated and cutting-edge programs in medicine, pain management, clinical immunology, MRI, biological response modifiers and molecular medicine were established. Roswell Park's new Flow Cytometry Laboratory, under the direction of Dr. Carleton Stewart, *opened its doors* to physicians and community leaders.

A Chemotherapy Clinic for adult outpatients included an outpatient pharmacy to allow on-site drug admixture and preparation of medications, as well as participation in patient education activities by a multidisciplinary team. In addition, Roswell Park expanded its Ambulatory Surgical Center to improve the efficiency of its surgical care and the level of comfort of patients and their families.

Dr. Nicholas Petrelli of the Division of Surgical Oncology also established a Department of Orthopedic Surgery to bolster the Institute's ability to deal with bone tumors and related orthopedic problems.

The Bone Marrow Transplant Unit was accredited by the National Marrow Donor Program as a marrow transplant and collection center in 1993. To Roswell Park, this designation meant that the Institute gained access to more than 900,000 potential donors in the National Registry, and was able to serve as a regional referral center for harvesting donor bone marrow cells.

A 600-hertz nuclear magnetic resonance spectrometer, one of only twenty such instruments in the United States, was installed, which enabled researchers to obtain the highest sensitivity available for structural studies in NMR.

Roswell Park and six area teaching hospitals joined with the University of Buffalo to develop a shared electronic information system to assist in patient care, research, and healthcare management. The system, called Hubnet, makes the equivalent of 6.5 million pages of medical data available through computer links.

The demolition of the Roswell Park Apartments to accommodate the Major Modernization Project required the relocation of 120 employees and ten business offices to the 38,000 square-foot, three-story, ninety-six-year-old building, on the corner of Main and Virginia Streets, that once housed the weekly newspaper of Buffalo's Catholic Diocese.

The Brain Tumor Treatment Center, a collaborative effort with the State University of New York at Buffalo, Millard Fillmore Hospital, and Buffalo General Hospital was established at Roswell Park to provide comprehensive treatment of all types of brain and spinal cord tumors in one centralized location in Western New York.

In addition, Roswell Park and Lake Shore Hospital established a joint program to offer free cancer screening examinations to residents in southern Erie, northern Chautauqua and western Cattaraugus Counties.

The Division of Radiation Medicine acquired a Therapax HF 150 Contact Therapy Unit, the first of its kind in Buffalo, to spare patients with easy-access tumors the pain and discomfort of surgery in favor of a simpler, less invasive radiation procedure.

**10-16.**

Roswell Park and the University of Buffalo entered a cooperative agreement regarding the use, site, and maintenance of the Institute's 4.7 Tesla magnetic resonance imager. Plans included establishing a new site for the MRI facility at Roswell Park, with use and operational costs shared jointly between the two institutions. Scientists from both Roswell and UB will have access to the MRI technology as well as the staff, supplies and services.

Roswell Park was awarded a $451,662 grant by the National Institutes of Health to develop 8,900 square feet of laboratory space in the Institute's new Medical Research Complex. The grant will fund completion of the construction of new centralized laboratory space for an Immunology Translational Research Program, which will contribute to the development of new drugs and therapies for patients with cancer and AIDS.

A Center for HIV-related Malignancies was established, under the direction of medical oncologist Dr. Zale Bernstein, to meet the special needs of patients who have cancer as a result of human immunodeficiency virus infection. The Center gives patients access to unique, cutting-edge therapies, several of which have been pioneered at Roswell Park. Subsequently, the Center was designated an "AIDS Treatment Center" by the New York State Health Department, making it the only such center in the State to exclusively treat AIDS-related cancers. The designation was conferred after a rigorous application process spanning almost two years.

Roswell Park opened a community cancer facility at 1616 Kensington Avenue in Buffalo to give residents easier access to its diagnostic, treatment and outreach programs.

In addition, the renewed interest in cryosurgery at Roswell Park translated into a viable therapeutic option for patients with primary and secondary liver cancers. In an effort to improve the dismal prognoses associated with these cancers, the Hepatic Cryosurgery Center was established.

On March 29, 1995, one hundred and twenty-five concrete trucks paraded down Carlton Street to the corner of Oak Street to pour 1,900 tons of concrete for the foundation of the Medical Research Complex component of the Major Modernization Project.

Roswell Park and the Millard Fillmore Health System opened the Ambulatory Cancer Care Center at Millard Fillmore Suburban Hospital in 1996. This facility ensures access to high quality cancer care to the 450,000 people in Millard's cachement area and provides a full range of outpatient cancer services, including chemotherapy and radiotherapy.

Roswell Park is online, with its World Wide Web site: http://rpci.med.buffalo.edu/ external.html to provide Internet access to the services of the Institute.

To promote the awareness of programs at Roswell Park, the circle of institutional affiliation widened at this time, enabling the Institute to broaden its own programs and contribute its experience to the formulation of various cancer programs nationwide as well. Roswell Park continued its affiliations with SUNY at Buffalo and many other academic institutions in the area. Nationally, the Institute continued its membership in the Association of American Cancer Institutes and, internationally, in the International Union Against Cancer. In 1996, Roswell Park became a member of the National Comprehensive Cancer Network, an alliance formed by leading cancer centers. This not-for-profit organization develops uniform, state-of-the-art practice guidelines for pediatric and adult cancers and measures to determine the clinical outcomes of treatments and their impact on quality of life.

Here are members of the Gratwick Society, who make annual contributions to Roswell Park Alliance Foundation of $1,000 or more, and in doing so they take a leadership position in supporting RPCI.

Mrs. Donna Gioia is chairperson of Gratwick Society. Present in picture are: Mrs. Anne Gioia, Mrs. Jane Crane, Dr. Mirand, Mrs. Donna Gioia, Mr. James Crane, Jr. (grandson of the original contributors of the Institute, Mrs. W. H. Gratwick), Mr. Roswell Park IV (great grandson of Dr. Roswell Park), Mr. and Mrs. Thomas Naples, and Dr. Thomas B. Tomasi.

Throughout the Tomasi administration, reference is made to the Roswell Park Alliance, which helped to support the mission of the Institute not only financially but also politically. How it was formed was a result of Anne Gioia's gratitude to the Institute in treating her five-year-old daughter for cancer.

In 1988, Anne Gioia's five-year-old daughter, Katherine, was treated for cancer but eventually died in July 1989. This loss inspired Anne and Donna Gioia to help other cancer patients and their families. As a result, the Roswell Park Alliance was founded on February 20, 1990, by Anne and Donna Gioia. The goals of this volunteer organization were to arrange community outreach programs and conduct fund-raising events and projects designed to enhance the quality of life of cancer patients and to raise community awareness of the accomplishments of the Institute. Fifty influential community leaders from Western New York became charter members. The extraordinary contributions made by the Roswell Park Alliance and the Roswell Park Alliance Foundation have resulted in substantial contributions from a variety of events. Roswell Park Cancer Institute is grateful to Director of Development Cindy Eller and the Alliance for their many efforts, including the following.

•The introduction of Wishing Well Holiday Cards which are designed by Roswell Park patients and friends. Roswell Park was the first hospital in Western New York to launch such a project. Over 100,000 cards are sold annually.

•The Roswell Park Alliance negotiated with Charles J. Palisano, a businessman from Orchard Park who lost six family members to cancer, a $1 million contribution to establish a laboratory dedicated to genetic research.

•The Roswell Park Alliance hosted its first Cancer Survivor Day, the Celebration of Your Life, on October 13, 1994. Over 500 current and former patients attended this gala event.

•The Roswell Park Alliance was the recipient of $3 million left by Mrs. Zelda Metzger to establish the Noma and Zelda C. Metzger Memorial Fund. This was the largest single bequest ever made to the Institute.

•Each year, the Roswell Park Alliance hosts All Star Night and its annual Cancer Drive. In 1997 this drive raised over $200,000. In 1996 General H. Norman Schwartzkopf (retired), who gained national prominence as commander of Operations Desert Shield and Desert Storm, received the Gilda Radner Courage Award at All Star Night. General Schwartzkopf is a prostate cancer survivor. In 1997 Marv Levy, vice president of Football Operations and head coach of the Buffalo Bills, received the same award in recognition of his personal battle with prostate cancer, which heightened public awareness of the disease. Coach Levy was treated at Roswell Park and has made it his mission to encourage early testing, especially those at high risk.

•Since its inception, the Roswell Park Alliance and the Gratwick Society together have raised close to $20 million to support patient care, research and education at Roswell Park.

Dr. Thomas B. Tomasi felt it was time to leave administration. Known as the *Scholarly Director*, he retired December 31, 1996. For ten years, from 1986 through 1996, he served as president and chief executive officer of Roswell Park Cancer Institute. He revitalized the Institute not only in repositioning the academic and clinical programs, but in tirelessly advocating for Roswell Park. Working with community leaders, he gained the support of endorsement of Governor Mario M. Cuomo and New York State legislators to construct the new $241 million hospital-research complex.

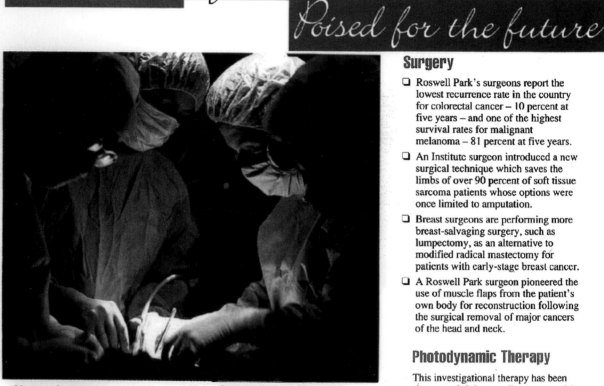

## Surgery

- ❑ Roswell Park's surgeons report the lowest recurrence rate in the country for colorectal cancer – 10 percent at five years – and one of the highest survival rates for malignant melanoma – 81 percent at five years.

- ❑ An Institute surgeon introduced a new surgical technique which saves the limbs of over 90 percent of soft tissue sarcoma patients whose options were once limited to amputation.

- ❑ Breast surgeons are performing more breast-salvaging surgery, such as lumpectomy, as an alternative to modified radical mastectomy for patients with early-stage breast cancer.

- ❑ A Roswell Park surgeon pioneered the use of muscle flaps from the patient's own body for reconstruction following the surgical removal of major cancers of the head and neck.

## Photodynamic Therapy

This investigational therapy has been shown to shrink or eradicate some of the most stubborn tumors, including those of the bladder, skin, breast, lung, brain, head and neck.

Pioneered at Roswell Park by Dr. Thomas Dougherty, Photodynamic Therapy combines tissue-penetrating red light and a non-toxic, light-sensitive chemical which, when injected into the body, remains in tumor tissue. Efficiently delivered through fiberoptics, the red light strikes the chemically-sensitized cancer cells and a tumor-destructive oxygen is released.

## Specialties of the House

Patient care innovations are part of Roswell Park's heritage.

- ❑ Establishment of Roswell Park's new **Bone Marrow Transplant Unit** means that Western New Yorkers will no longer have to travel to distant cities for this cutting-edge treatment. The bone marrow transplant team plans to perform about 150 procedures annually.

- ❑ Patients with cancer may experience pain before or during the course of treatment. Roswell Park offers a multidisciplinary **Pain Management Program** that develops and applies new techniques for controlling and alleviating pain.

## Chemotherapy

Our researchers and clinicians continue to search for new drugs and ways to make existing drugs more effective.

- ❑ Roswell Park has contributed significantly to the improved survival rates of childhood cancer patients. One successful treatment, pioneered at the Institute, using the drug methotrexate, has improved survival rates for childhood leukemia from 50 percent to 75 percent.

- ❑ The highest potential cure rates for advanced ovarian cancer were reported by Roswell Park physicians who treat the disease with a highly effective combination of agents.

- ❑ New chemotherapeutic agents and new approaches to the use of standard drugs are being evaluated in patients with blood disorders who have exhausted conventional treatments. The lives of many of these patients have been saved or extended through their participation in these studies.

### Radiotherapy

- ❑ Radiologists at Roswell Park have introduced two new and more effective ways of delivering radiation – **stereotactic radiation** and **brachytherapy**. These sophisticated treatment methods are used to treat recurrent malignant brain tumors and recurrent, inoperable lung cancer, respectively.

## Combined Treatments

Roswell Park has also seen a number of successes in combining different types of treatment:

- ❑ One treatment uses the anticancer drug hydroxyurea to enhance the effects of radiation. This therapy has improved the survival rates of women with advanced cervical cancer from 37 percent to 94 percent.

- ❑ By their pioneering use of a radiation implant following hysterectomy, our gynecologic oncologists have achieved the highest cure rate in the country for uterine cancer.

- ❑ Clinical studies which combine chemotherapy with surgery have resulted in improved survival rates for patients with advanced bladder cancer.

- ❑ Doctors are using sequential endocrine therapy and chemotherapy to successfully treat metastatic breast cancer.

- ❑ Roswell Park was one of the first facilities in the country to study and test the effects of hyperthermia, an investigational therapy that uses heat in combination with other treatments, such as radiation, to destroy cancer cells.

❏ Roswell Park is the only facility in upstate New York State to offer **photopheresis**, a new cancer treatment for cutaneous T-cell lymphoma (CTCL), an extremely debilitating and potentially fatal disease of white blood cells. Approved by the FDA, photopheresis uses a drug which is activated by the administration of ultraviolet A radiation.

❏ The **Center for Experimental Therapeutics**, an NCI-recognized specialized cancer drug center within Roswell Park, is one of only two centers in the United States which has the capability of taking drug development from its conceptual stage through manufacture and testing of the compound.

❏ The nation's first **Plateletpheresis Donor Center** was established at Roswell Park in 1964. This service supplies blood platelets to leukemia patients who are prone to hemorrhaging.

❏ A **Long-term Follow-up Clinic,** one of the first of its kind in the nation, was created to provide specialized medical care and counseling to former childhood cancer patients. Dramatic success in the treatment of childhood cancers has resulted in a population of survivors who may have unique problems, such as difficulty in finding employment, questions concerning their reproductive capability because of their cancer and its treatment, and the possibility of developing other malignancies later in life. This clinic assists cancer survivors in building full and productive lives.

❏ Roswell Park was one of the first institutions to establish a **Cancer Prevention-Detection Center** which offers *free* cancer screening to the public. Each year, nearly 6,000 individuals receive a physical examination designed to detect early cancers.

❏ Roswell Park is the headquarters of the **Regional Center for Maxillofacial Prosthetics,** one of only a dozen such centers in the United States. Prostheses, artificial devices to replace missing parts of the body, are custom-designed to help rehabilitate cancer and trauma patients with head and neck defects or injuries.

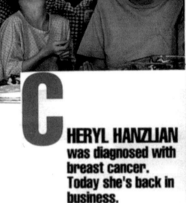

**C**HERYL HANZLIAN was diagnosed with breast cancer. Today she's back in business.

Cheryl Hanzlian was working a busy schedule at her boutique in Sackett's Harbor, New York, when she found out she had breast cancer in the fall of 1990. After the first physician she saw recommended a mastectomy, Cheryl went to Roswell Park for a second opinion.

*Roswell was a God-send,* says Cheryl. *I told my doctor 'I need you to give me advice as if I were your wife.' He really took the time to explain my options to me, and I chose to have a lumpectomy with chemotherapy. Now, I'm running my own business again. I just can't say enough about the expert care at Roswell.*

**10-19.**

Senior staff members
of Grace Cancer Drug
Center picnic at Evangola
State Park in 1986. Left
to right: Drs. Ralph
Bernacki, Molly Kulesz-
Martin, Carl Porter,
John McGuire, and
Janice Suffrin.

BARBARA A. DeBUONO, M.D., M.P.H.
Commissioner

Phone: (518) 474-2011
Fax: (518) 474-5450

December 6, 1995

Dear Members of the RPCI Senior Medical and Scientific Staff:

As you know, Dr. Tomasi has submitted his resignation to me effective January 1, 1997. It is with regret that I have accepted Dr. Tomasi's resignation.

Since Dr. Tomasi's arrival at Roswell Park Cancer Institute in 1986, he has made many remarkable and significant contributions to the stature of this outstanding Institute. Roswell Park enjoys an international reputation for excellence in patient care and scientific research and is extremely well supported by the community. As you well know, Roswell Park was recently honored once again by U.S. News and World Report magazine as one of the top cancer hospitals in the country. Dr. Tomasi and the Roswell staff are to be congratulated for the effort put forth in achieving this enviable status.

You realize that these are difficult times for Roswell Park Cancer Institute as well as the entire health care industry. 1996 will be a year that will challenge all of us who have key roles in the delivery of health care. As President and CEO, Dr. Tomasi will continue his leadership role and full responsibilities until the effective date of his resignation. Dr. Tomasi has my support and he will need the support from the entire staff at Roswell Park to ensure a productive 1996.

We will begin a national search to identify a new president and CEO who will pick up the leadership from Dr. Tomasi and continue to lead the Institute as we go forward toward the 21st century. Thanks to the advance notice provided, we should be able to enjoy an orderly and smooth transition of the leadership of Roswell Park. Please join me in thanking Dr. Tomasi for his many years of dedicated service and by providing your continued support of the Institute during this transition period.

Roswell Park must remain a steady and financially viable facility during this very trying time when health care as we know it is undergoing very significant change. We must be prepared to meet the challenge so we can continue to provide quality health care to the citizens of our great state in an efficient manner. We no longer can do business as usual. I will need your continued help and support as we guide our way through this different health care environment.

Very truly yours,

Barbara DeBuono

Barbara A. DeBuono, M.D., M.P.H.
Commissioner of Health

**10-20.**

New York State
Commissioner of
Health Dr. Barbara
DeBuono announces
the retirement of
Dr. Thomas B. Tomasi.

Dr. Tomasi has returned to the laboratory in Molecular Medicine at Roswell Park, working with Drs. Peter D. Aplan, Michael Caligiuri, Sharon Evans, A. Latif Kazim, Sara Schneider, and Meir Wetzler. More recently Dr. Tomasi and his laboratory staff have discovered an immuno-suppressive factor at the fetal-maternal interface that regulates key genes involved in reproduction. These studies offer great promise in explaining critical regulatory steps in immunity in transplantation, cancer, and autoimmune diseases. On October 15, 1997, SUNY at Buffalo conferred an Honorary Doctorate Degree recognizing the scholarly dedication of Dr. Tomasi, who has authored over 250 scientific publications, as administrator and scientist.

Prior to Dr. Tomasi's retirement, State Health Commissioner Dr. Barbara A. DeBuono appointed a Search Committee headed by Dr. Harold Freeman, chairman of the President's Cancer Panel, to conduct a national search for a successor to Dr. Tomasi.

# Chapter 11

The Hennessy Interval:
Gordon Hennessy, MHA

1997

In January 1997 New York State Health
Commissioner Dr. Barbara A. DeBuono appointed
Mr. Gordon Hennessy, MHA, director of facilities
management for the Department of Health, interim
president, and CEO. Mr. Hennessy traveled from
Albany to Buffalo to spend at least three days each
week at the Institute reviewing issues with Ms. C.
Angela Bontempo, Dr. Jerome W. Yates and other
members of the administration.

**11-1**
Mr. Gordon Hennessy.

**12-1.**
Dr. David C. Hohn
with Governor George
E. Pataki on October
15, 1997.

present

**12-2.**
NYS Commissioner
of Health Dr. Barbara
DeBuono addresses
an audience on
October 15, 1997.

In mid-February, the farsighted New York State Commissioner of Health, Dr. Barbara A. DeBuono, announced the appointment of Dr. David C. Hohn, a surgical oncologist and former vice president for patient care at the University of Texas M.D. Anderson Cancer Center. Dr. Hohn, who was selected following a national search and the review of over forty candidates, played a major role in the Center's re-engineering and strategic planning processes and in legislative initiatives that allowed the facility to adapt to changes in healthcare and respond to the expanded role of managed care. Dr. Hohn is a summa cum laude graduate of the University of Illinois School of Medicine, and completed his surgical residency at the University of California, San Francisco. He worked at M. D. Anderson since 1987, serving in a number of clinical and administrative positions. *I am committed to preserving and enhancing Roswell Park's well-deserved reputation for excellence in cancer research, patient care and prevention,* said Dr. Hohn. *I have come to Buffalo to lead and serve Roswell Park, not to sell it, and to build the Institute so that it not only survives, but thrives.*

**12-3.**

Dr. David Hohn, immediately upon his arrival, assured the staff and the community that "Roswell Park is not for sale" and that he was committed to fulfilling its mission as leading comprehensive cancer center.

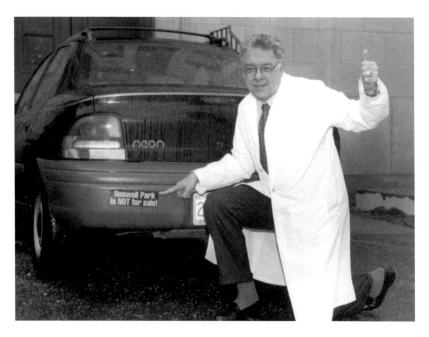

Dr. Hohn's immediate goals are to . . .

•work with the Health Commissioner, Governor George E. Pataki, the New York State legislature, and the staff of Roswell Park to effectuate governance changes necessary for the Institute's viability.

•initiate a comprehensive review of clinical and research programs and develop a plan for excellence to serve as a template for the Institute's continued commitment to cutting edge research and the highest quality patient care.

•develop a strategic marketing plan to expand Roswell Park's market share beyond Buffalo to neighboring states and other niche cancer markets.

•develop a five-year fund raising initiative that has goals for future endowments to help support long-term capitalization and research activities.

Representing an extraordinary collaborative effort from Roswell Park (particularly Dr. Hohn, with Ms. Barbara Howard), the New York State Department of Health (particularly Dr. DeBuono), Governor George E. Pataki and the Governor's Office of Employee Relations, union leadership and the WNY Delegation, Senate Majority Leader Joseph Bruno, Assembly Majority Leader Sheldon Silver, new legislation (Chapter 5, Laws of 1997) was passed unanimously which provides for a public health and research corporation to run Roswell Park (while maintaining civil service protections for its employees). The legislation, which was introduced by State Senator Dale M. Volker and Deputy Assembly Speaker Arthur O. Eve, gives Roswell Park the flexibility it needs to compete in the changing healthcare climate.

In announcing the enactment of the budget and passage of his Program Bill on August 4, 1997, New York State Governor George E. Pataki assures the citizens of Western New York that Roswell Park will have "a long and successful future in providing compassionate cancer care and groundbreaking research."

Specifically, the legislation . . .

• creates the Roswell Park Cancer Institute Corporation (RPCIC) with a fifteen-member Board of Directors appointed by the Governor and legislature.

• establishes RPCIC as an employer in the NYS Employees Retirement System, ensures employees transferring to the corporation are protected by the state Civil Service Law with the same rights, benefits, and collective bargaining unit designations they had as state employees, and continues their protections under the Public Officers' Law.

• allows RPCIC to participate in managed care networks and other joint and cooperative arrangements for the provision of comprehensive and specialty healthcare services.

• allows RPCIC to establish subsidiary corporations to meet the demands of a changing healthcare market and to develop and market products or services through its clinical/research activities.

• authorizes the Health Commissioner to execute an agreement for the transfer of the operations of Roswell Park Cancer Institute to Roswell Park Cancer Institute Corporation.

**12-4.**

Governor George E. Pataki signing RPCI Corporation Bill. Left to right: Assemblyman Robin Schimminger, Senator George Maziarz, and Attorney General Dennis Vacco. To the Governor's right is Senator Dale Volker and to his left Assemblyman Arthur Eve.

**12-6.**

Governor George Pataki signs our Guest Book on the occasion of October 15, 1997.

**12-5.**

Governor George Pataki is congratulated after signing RPCI Corporation Bill.

The Governor came to the Institute on October 15, 1997, to sign the bill previously passed by the New York State Assembly and Senate to transfer Roswell Park out of the New York State Department of Health and become a Public Benefit Corporation. (The Roswell Park Cancer Institute Governance Study released by Coopers & Lybrand on February 3, 1996, presented an analysis of organizational options for Roswell Park. One option was to become a Public Benefit Corporation, another was to become an affiliate of the University at Buffalo and still another was to become a voluntary organization 501 (c)(3), not-for-profit. All parties reviewing these three options felt the Public Benefit Corporation was more meritorious).

# Aid hike proposed for Roswell Park

## Pataki's spending plan to include 25 percent increase for area cancer institute

**By TOM PRECIOUS**
*News Albany Bureau*

ALBANY — The state's financial commitment to Roswell Park Cancer Institute will increase by more than 25 percent in the coming year under a budget proposal to be unveiled Tuesday by Gov. Pataki.

As it undergoes its transformation into a quasi-public corporation de-signed to make it more competitive with other health-care institutions, Roswell Park will see its funding from Albany rise to $103.6 million, up from the current year funding of $76 million, Pataki administration sources said Monday.

State officials say the extra money will help the once-struggling Roswell Park to again become one of the nation's premier cancer research hospitals.

"I'm extremely grateful and heart-ened by the support the governor has shown," said Roswell Park's president and chief executive officer, Dr. David Hohn.

The governor's complete, election-year budget will be released today at the Capitol. Over the past few days, Pataki has already put out details on some of the more politically popular areas of the budget. Continuing that trend, the governor Monday said he would ask the Legislature to spend $400 million in the coming year on a host of construction projects for the State University of New York and the City University of New York.

And while Pataki has no plans to reduce SUNY tuition, as some groups have called for, administration aides said he would propose to double the number of so-called merit scholarships.

*1/20/98*

## Roswell Park: Extra funds to help transition

*Continued from Page A1*

worth $500 a year, to 6,000.

Besides $15.6 million for construction projects at the University at Buffalo and Buffalo State College, the governor's office said a number of other western New York SUNY facilities are in line for major capital funding programs. The money is especially aimed at bolstering the technological abilities of the public colleges.

On the arts front, Pataki said Monday he would ask for a 12.4 percent increase in spending. His aides declined to provide details, with the exception of a $350,000 grant for the New York City Ballet Company to tour selected SUNY campuses.

The funding for Roswell Park comes at a critical time for the facility. Hohn, the Roswell Park chief, said the additional money Pataki is proposing will help pay for a number of costs associated with its transition from a state institution to a so-called public benefit corporation.

Under a state law approved last year, Roswell Park will now be able to negotiate terms with its unionized workers, enter into deals with other health-care providers and set up regional subsidiaries.

Hohn said some of the money will fund Roswell Park's move into a new building later this spring, as well as to begin to offer training programs for workers in everything from finance to computer technology. He said the funds will help upgrade Roswell Park's aging computer systems and to attract world-class scientists to head up some of the facility's research offices. Some of its science programs have been run by interim directors for years.

"This will help us jump-start our science programs," Hohn said of the recruitment efforts.

"In the past, the Western New York delegation has had to work very hard at making sure Roswell Park has gotten its appropriate and necessary funding," said State

**With the state flush with a more than $1 billion surplus in its current fiscal year that ends March 31, Pataki's budget — if the past few days of budget leaks from his administration are any indication — will be anything but austere.**

Assembly Republican leader Thomas Reynolds of Springville. "This is an effort to show continued support of Roswell Park. At this point, we're off to a pretty good start in the funding."

With the state flush with a more than $1 billion surplus in its current fiscal year that ends March 31, Pataki's budget — if the past few days of budget leaks from his administration is any indication — will be anything but austere.

Monday's announcement of a $400 million capital program for SUNY and City University of New York will lead to a massive building campaign throughout the state's public university system. But it also will, observers note, help deflect criticism Democrats have been tossing at Pataki as an enemy of SUNY. Pataki, in the past three years, has pushed through a tuition hike, financial-aid cuts and reduced funding for SUNY programs that have hit some colleges especially hard.

In Western New York, the governor proposes:

■ Alfred State College — $10 million for a complete rehabilitation of its 30-year-old engineering technology building, as well as another $2.8 million to rebuild roads and sidewalks and to renovate classrooms with more high-technology equipment.

■ New York State College of Ceramics, located at Alfred University — $12 million to renovate the Binns-Merrill Hall.

"This will make a quantum jump in the goal, scope and expectations of our programs," said L. David Pye, dean of the college.

He said the money will be used to bring the building, built in 1951, up to code in a number of areas, as well as to build new lab facilities for carrying out research in ceramic-related materials.

■ Geneseo State College — $20 million for a complete rehabilitation of the Bailey Science Building, to include construction of state-of-the-art lab facilities.

"This really is a central priority for us," said Geneseo's president, Christopher Dahl.

■ Fredonia State College — $3.1 million for replacing an underground water distribution system, installation of fiber-optic cabling and other work to upgrade its technology offerings and sidewalk replacement.

■ UB — a share of a statewide $7.3 million fund to replace aging transformers that contain PCBs. UB also is slated to receive an as-yet undetermined amount of money in the 1999-2000 state budget to renovate the Farber Health Education Center on the South Campus on Main Street.

SUNY campuses throughout New York will be getting face lifts under Pataki's budget. At New Paltz State College, $400,000 would go for a day-care center, while Stony Brook would get nearly $10 million for a new stadium.

William E. Scheurman, president of United University Professions, the SUNY professors' union, praised Pataki's capital construction proposals.

"The next test of the executive's commitment will be (today's) release of the all-important state operating budget. The state must invest equally in SUNY's academic programs, or they will suffer the same fate as SUNY's buildings and grounds," he said.

In the Hilleboe Auditorium, in the presence of the Western New York legislative delegation, the Roswell Park Alliance, other community leaders and staff, Governor George E. Pataki commented, *Our commitment to ensuring that Roswell Park remains a leader in cancer research, treatment and education is unwavering. Many people, including Senator Dale Volker, Republican Assembly Leader Thomas Reynolds, Assemblyman Arthur Eve, have made it a priority to ensure that this facility can survive and prosper. I am confident that this legislation means the second 100 years of Roswell Park will not only be as good but better than the first 100 years.*

Dr. Barbara A. DeBuono said: *What I am hoping for the future is that Roswell will be not only the preeminent and number one cancer institute in this country—I also want to see in* U.S. News and World Report *in the year 2000 that the number one cancer institute is Roswell Park Cancer Institute.*

To commemorate the 100th Anniversary, Dr. David Hohn appointed Dr. Edwin A. Mirand as chairman of the 100th Anniversary Committee, assisted by Mrs. Cynthia Schwartz, serving as co-chair. The Committee to assist Dr. Mirand and Mrs. Schwartz in planning events to celebrate the occasion were: Dr. John Brooks, Kevin A. Craig, Laurel DiBrog, Cindy Eller, Barbara Howard, Linda Kahn, Colleen M. Karuza, Dr. Enrico Mihich, Dr. Youcef Rustum, Dr. Donald Shedd, Daniel I. Sheff, Dr. Yasmin Thanavala, Erin Wright, and Dr. Jerome Yates.

A number of events have been planned throughout 1998, including the Immunology Conference, February 19–20 and the Cancer Genetics and Biology Seminar, October 8–9. There will be a series of named lectures, including the Curie, Cori, Roswell Park, and Clowes lectures. There will be a special insert in the BUFFALO NEWS CENTENNIAL MAGAZINE on April 26. The dedication of the new building will be May 22. A Roswell Park Alumni Reunion is scheduled for October 10, and the President's Cancer Panel will meet at the Institute in October. The Historical Society Exhibit is scheduled for the fall and there will be receptions at major meetings (AACR, ASCO, UICC, and the American College of Surgeons). The Alliance Foundation is planning a number of events as well, including All Star Night on February 21 and the Celebration of Life on June 7, 1998.

On February 1, 1997, New York State First Lady Libby Pataki, Congressman Jack Quinn, Senator Mary Lou Rath and Assemblyman Thomas Reynolds were among the VIPs attending the opening of the Western New York Breast Resource Center at Roswell Park. Under the direction of Dr. Steven Edge, Department of Breast Surgery, this important community resource—made possible through the coordinated, collective efforts of support groups, corporate sponsors, volunteer organizations, and Roswell Park—is a clearinghouse of information on all topics relating to breast cancer and breast health. On October 22, 1997, she revisited the Center to promote its activities.

**12-8.**
Dr. David Hohn addresses staff on his mission goals for the Institute on December 18, 1997.

**12-9.**
Staff photograph on December 18, 1997, with Dr. David Hohn.

Some outstanding appointments have already been made by Dr. David C. Hohn: Ms. Barbara Howard, vice president for Governmental Relations; Mrs. Laurel DiBrog, vice president for Marketing and Planning; Ms. Pamela Germain, vice president for Managed Care and Outreach; Mr. Anthony Woods, director of Classification and Compensation; Mr. Michael Sexton, general counsel; and Dr. Lawrence Leichman succeeded Dr. Clara Bloomfield as chairman of the Division of Medicine. On December 18, 1997, Dr. Arthur Michalek was appointed chair of the Department of Education Affairs replacing the retired Dr. Edwin A. Mirand. Dr. Mirand had served for over five decades in a number of administrative and scientific posts and will continue as a volunteer at the Institute as Senior advisor to the President and CEO and as director of the Alumni and Archive Office.

As Dr. Hohn implements his plans, he sees Roswell Park Cancer Institute as a mecca of hope, with a dedicated staff involved in solving the intricate riddle of cancer that will have played no small role in the final victory over cancer. In addressing the staff in a President's Report, he stated: *No doubt, there is a sense of excitement and anticipation among the staff as the new campus takes shape. Program leaders in the basic science and clinical areas and education have worked diligently to build a foundation for the future that is of high quality, innovative and compassionate. This foundation will allow us to advance cancer research, cure more cancer patients, educate the public on cancer prevention, and prepare the next generation of cancer specialists. I am thoroughly impressed by the vision and scope of what is being done and what is being accomplished in these programs.*

*However, there is also a sense of apprehension among the staff as we prepare for the future. It may not be enough anymore for academic institutions such as Roswell Park to be considered Centers of Excellence and Comprehensive Cancer Centers. It may not be enough to be competitive for research grants and contracts that underpin progress in cancer research.*

*It may not be enough unless Roswell Park rapidly adopts new business approaches which will enable it to survive and thrive in a healthcare environment driven more by economics than science and medicine. Roswell Park will need to successfully compete for clinical referrals and for grants and contracts. A new approach to the competitive healthcare marketplace that does not lose sight of our mission of cancer research, treatment and education is being developed. The challenge is daunting. The many strengths of Roswell Park's faculty and staff, and their high level of dedication to meeting these challenges make me absolutely confident that we will succeed.*

*The historical parallel is interesting. When Dr. Roswell Park was looking for a new approach to studying and treating cancer in 1898, he relied on New York State, his professional colleagues and the community to forge his dream of creating a laboratory dedicated exclusively to cancer research. Today, we are again relying on New York State, on our colleagues locally and nationally and on our extraordinarily supportive community to forge our dream of recreating Roswell Park Cancer Institute.*

*Working together, I am confident that we can and will succeed. Roswell Park will enter the twenty-first century even stronger and better able to respond to the needs of its patients and staff and to the demands of a changing healthcare arena.*

# Epilogue

As the plans for the changes that will take place unfold, we must all realize that we live in the great, dynamic web of change. It links us to one another and in some ways, everything in the past and in the way that each of us influences the course of events. It also links us to the future we are all busy making at the Institute. No matter how far all those links may seem, no person acts without causing change on the web. Each one of us has an effect somewhere. Everybody contributes to the process of change. In some way, anything we do makes history because we are history. The web of change is the expression of our existence and of all those who have gone before and all of those who will come after us who will be engaged in contributing to Dr. Park's original ambition to see cancer conquered.

# Appendices

**1898**    **Chapter 606, page 1449**
Governor Frank S. Black signs bill April 29, 1898, establishing the New York State Pathological Laboratory of the University of Buffalo located in the University of Buffalo Medical School on High Street.

**1911**    **Chapter 128**
The Gratwick Research Laboratory became a New York State institute. LAWS OF NEW YORK STATE, Chapter 128, May 10, 1911. This legislation included provisions for New York State to accept properties.

**1912**
The University of Buffalo officially transfered the Gratwick Research Laboratory to New York State February 29, 1912, and deeded the parcel of land at High and Oak Streets (Liber 1239 of Deeds at page 309), on which the Gratwick Research Laboratory was built, to the State on March 12, 1912. The Gratwick Research Laboratory was renamed the New York State Institute for the Study of Malignant Disease.

State Senate Bill 75 further provided for a Board of Trustees and for the organization of the Institute.

New Board of Trustees formed composed of Dr. Roswell Park (Buffalo), Dr. Charles Cary (Buffalo), Mr. John Milburn (New York City), Mr. William H. Gratwick (Buffalo), Mr. Frederick C. Steven (Utica) and the Honorable Charles S. Fairchild (New York City).

**1926**    **Chapter 349**
The Institute was brought under the management and control of the newly formed New York State Department of Health (effective January 1, 1927). Board of Trustees was renamed Board of Visitors.

**1927**    **Chapter 48**
New York State Institute for the Study of Malignant Diseases became a new Article 18 under the Public Health Law. Repealed parts of Ch. 349 L. 26 incorporated them into the new Article 18 of the Public Health Law.

**1931**    **Chapter 481**
State Institute for the Study of Malignant Diseases continued and a new division of Cancer Control was created within the Institute, headed by Dr. Louis C. Kress in 1932. This was later moved to Albany.

**1939**    **Chapter 168**
Institute Annual Reports were required by the New York State Commissioner of Health.

**1944**    **Chapter 298**
Section 9—Institute continued. Section 11—Adds new Article 18-A to Public Health Law (Cancer Control Division).

**1946**    **Chapter 369**
Renamed Insitute to Roswell Park Memorial Institute by initiation of a Dr. J. Galvin Woodworth and Assemblyman William Butler.

**1992**    **Chapter 293**
New York State authorizes on August 11, 1992, bonding for major renovation and new construction projects collectively called the RPCI Major Modernization Project. The $241.5 million project is the largest hospital investment ever approved for a New York State facility.

Name of Institute officially changed from Roswell Park Memorial Institute to Roswell Park Cancer Institute.

**1995**    **Chapter 505**
The Department of Health Flexibility Bill provides the Institute with needed flexibility to establish managed care contracts and added local purchasing authority.

**1997**    **Chapter 5**
Roswell Park Cancer Institute Corporation Act is signed into law, authorizing the creation of a Public Benefit Corporation to operate Roswell Park, ending seventy years as a facility of the New York State Department of Health.

# The Heritage of Carl and Gerty Cori at Roswell Park Cancer Institute

(Note: Numbers in parenthesis refer to correspondingly numbered sections of the diagram on page 178.)

Our understanding of the nature of cancer and of how to treat the disease has advanced dramatically since Roswell Park (1) established the Gratwick Research Laboratory one hundred years ago. Scientists at the Gratwick Research Laboratory, the New York State Institute for the Study of Malignant Diseases, Roswell Park Memorial Institute, and Roswell Park Cancer Institute have contributed significantly to every step in this advance, but no contribution has been so profound or far-reaching as that made by Carl and Gerty Cori during their nine years at the Institute [1922–1931 (3)] and their continuation of this work at Washington University in St. Louis [1931–1966 (4)]. Their investigations, which led to a joint Nobel Prize in 1947 (5), laid the groundwork for more recent studies which have established that cancer is a consequence of genetic mutations that destroy normal cellular regulatory mechanisms, permitting unregulated invasive cell growth.

Dr. Harvey Gaylord (2), the second Institute director, was also one of the first to realize the importance of studying cancer biochemically. To promote such studies, he scoured Europe after World War I looking for good biochemists who were interested in studying cancer and who might wish to escape European postwar economic and political uncertainties by emigrating to the USA. The European scientists that Dr. Gaylord consulted gave rave reviews to a young, German-speaking Czech husband and wife team, Carl and Gerty Cori. When Gaylord approached the Coris, he found them excited about the possibility, so he quickly finalized all necessary arrangements. The Coris sailed for the USA in 1922.

Once established at the Institute, the Coris (3) began experimenting and publishing at a rapid rate. Their major interest was not in cancer *per se,* but in learning how cells get energy from sugars and sugar compounds (carbohydrates). They had good reason, however, to think that characterizing the ways in which cells turn sugar and sugar compounds into energy [a process call carbohydrate metabolism (6)] might well prove useful in understanding cancer: German biochemist Otto Warburg had just shown that certain tumor cells in the test tube obtain energy by a rapid but inefficient process called glycolysis, as opposed to the slower but more efficient process called respiration by which normal cells primarily derive their energy. Since the Coris had access to real tumors at the Institute, they were able to demonstrate that Warburg's test tube discovery also applies to corresponding real tumors in human cancer patients. [Note: Subsequent work by Charles Wenner (23), a current Roswell Park Cancer Institute scientist, has shown that elevated glycolysis is not a general property of all tumors.]

At the Institute, the Coris established three major areas of research about carbohydrate metabolism: [i] how are excess sugars stored in the liver as *animal starch* [glycogen] at times when energy needs are low, and how is glycogen broken down into sugar which can then be further metabolized to provide energy at times when energy needs are high (7), [ii] how is this process regulated by the hormone's insulin [which promotes sugar storage] and epinephrine [which promotes the release of sugar from glycogen] (8), and [iii] what are the enzymes [proteins that serve as biological catalysts] that promote these properties, and how are those enzymes regulated (9).

In 1931, the Coris left the Institute for Washington University in St. Louis (4). [It's interesting that the reason for their departure was the same as cited by many scientists who have left in recent years: insufficient funding. Had the Coris stayed, developments described in the following paragraphs would have taken place in Buffalo instead of St. Louis, with perhaps profound implications for the Buffalo economy!] In St. Louis, each of the lines of research initiated at the Institute came to fruition.

In pursuit of the mechanism by which glycogen is synthesized and broken down, the Coris discovered the enzyme *glycogen phosphorylase.* Within the liver and muscle, where glycogen is stored, phosphorylase catalyzes glycogen breakdown into sugar. But, the Coris showed, this enzyme can also catalyze glycogen synthesis by reversal of the breakdown reaction. Their demonstration of glycogen synthesis in the test tube showed, for the first time, that synthesis of biological macromolecules, like the synthesis of small biological molecules, can be accomplished in the laboratory and does not require any mystical *force* present only in living organisms. This was the final nail in the coffin of *vitalism* theories.

The Coris' prowess in studying carbohydrate metabolism and macromolecules attracted other biochemists to Washington University, including Arthur Kornberg, who utilized many of the principles elucidated by the Coris to discover the enzymatic mechanism of DNA synthesis (10). [Note that DNA, like glycogen, is a polymer containing sugars.] Another biochemist who migrated to Washington University was Paul Berg, who subsequently characterized the mechanism of RNA synthesis (11). Kornberg, Berg and several other Washington University biochemists were later recruited by Stanford University, where they established the Biochemistry Department whose joint discoveries paved the way for gene cloning, the modern biotechnology industry and much of modern molecular biology.

Joel Huberman (13), a current scientist at Roswell Park Cancer Institute, was a postdoctoral student of Arthur Kornberg. Huberman has contributed significantly to our understanding of DNA synthesis in human cells by his discovery and contributions to the characterization of DNA replication origins (12), the places on DNA molecules where the process of DNA synthesis begins. Because cancer cells proliferate uncontrollably, and because proliferation requires DNA synthesis, improved understanding of the regulation of DNA synthesis (17) is required if we are to fully understand the differences between cancer cells and normal cells. One important component of the regulation of DNA synthesis is the replication origin (12). Other current Roswell Park Cancer Institute scientists also have contributed significantly to the characterization of such origins. David Kowalski (14) discovered the importance for origin function of DNA sequences that are easily unwound. John Yates (15) discovered the replication origin of the virus that causes mononucleosis and some cancers. And, Bill Burhans (16) developed methods important for the characterization of replication origins in human cells.

Let's turn to the Coris' other interests, the action of hormones (8) and the regulation of enzymes (9). Current Roswell Park Cancer Institute scientist, Tom Shows, has helped extend the Coris' characterization of insulin by locating the position of the insulin gene within human chromosomes (18). Post-Cori studies in many other laboratories throughout the world have demonstrated that hormone action, in general, is the result of several steps. First, hormones bind to specific receptors on the cell membrane. Second, this binding stimulates a specific signalling pathway within the cell (19), and the signalling pathway ultimately leads to specific intracellular effects. It is now known that hormones regulate many cellular processes, including the cell division cycle (20).

The Coris' students, Earl Sutherland and Edwin Krebs, and Krebs' later coworker, Edmund Fischer, continued the Coris' studies of regulation (9) of the glycogen breakdown enzyme, phosphorylase (7). They discovered that the enzyme, phosphorylase, could be converted from an inactive form to an active form by the addition of a phosphate group to the inactive form. Addition of the phosphate was catalyzed by a second enzyme, phosphorylase kinase. A third enzyme, phosphorylase phosphate, could remove the phosphate and thereby restore the inactive form (21). Subsequent work has shown that many other cellular enzymes are also regulated by phosphorylation/dephosphorylation. In particular, both pathways that carry signals from hormones within cells (19) and the cell division cycle (20) depend on cascades of phosphorylation and dephosphorylation (21).

Dr. Charles Helmstetter (22), who recently retired from Roswell Park Cancer Institute, was a pioneer in studies of cell division cycle regulation [the mechanisms regulating the timing of DNA synthesis and cell division so that these processes take place in correct order] (20). Regulation of the cell cycle is intimately connected to the cell's decision to divide or not to divide. Since unregulated cell division [unregulated cell proliferation] is an essential feature of cancer, improved understanding of how the cell cycle is regulated is essential for dealing with the cancer problem. For that reason, a number of current Roswell Park scientists are building on the earlier studies of the Coris and their students—particularly their demonstration of the importance of hormones and of phosphorylation—to understand cell cyle regulation in cancer and normal cells.

Roswell Park scientists Charles Wenner (23) and Alexander Bloch (24) are studying the effects of hormones on the rate of cell division, as mediated by signalling pathways that involve phosphorylation. Also, Jane Azizkhan (25) is elucidating the mechanisms by which genes required for DNA synthesis are activated in the cell cycle just before DNA synthesis takes place. Three investigators—Molly Kulesz-Martin (26), Bill Burhans (27) and Joel Huberman (28)—are studying cell cycle checkpoints, which are regulatory mechanisms that prevent cell cycle progression when DNA is damaged or when a preceding cell cycle phase is not yet complete. All of these investigations lead to information useful in understanding how antitumor drugs affect cell proliferation and how they target cell cycle regulatory defects in cancer cells to specifically kill such cancer cells (29).

Hormones do more than regulate the cell cycle. Heinz Bauman (30) of Roswell Park has discovered the set of hormones that mediate the body's response to tissue injury. Cancer injures normal tissues, so Baumann is investigating how the tissue injury response might be modified to help the body fight cancer. Similarly, Thomas Tomasi (31) is investigating ways in which normal responses to hormones by the immune system can be modified to strengthen the immune system and help it to attack cancer cells. Since cancers are occasionally cured as a consequence of the body's natural defenses, finding ways to strengthen those defenses (32) seems a promising strategy in our efforts to conquer this disease.

Thus, the Coris' accomplishments have had a profound impact on many areas of cancer research. It is sobering to recall that the Coris' primary interest was not in cancer but in basic metabolic processes, common to most living organisms. That is why it is important, even today, to continue to support basic research. One can never predict which discoveries in basic research will prove to have consequences for fighting cancer and other human ailments as significant as those of the Coris' investigations of carbohydrate metabolism.

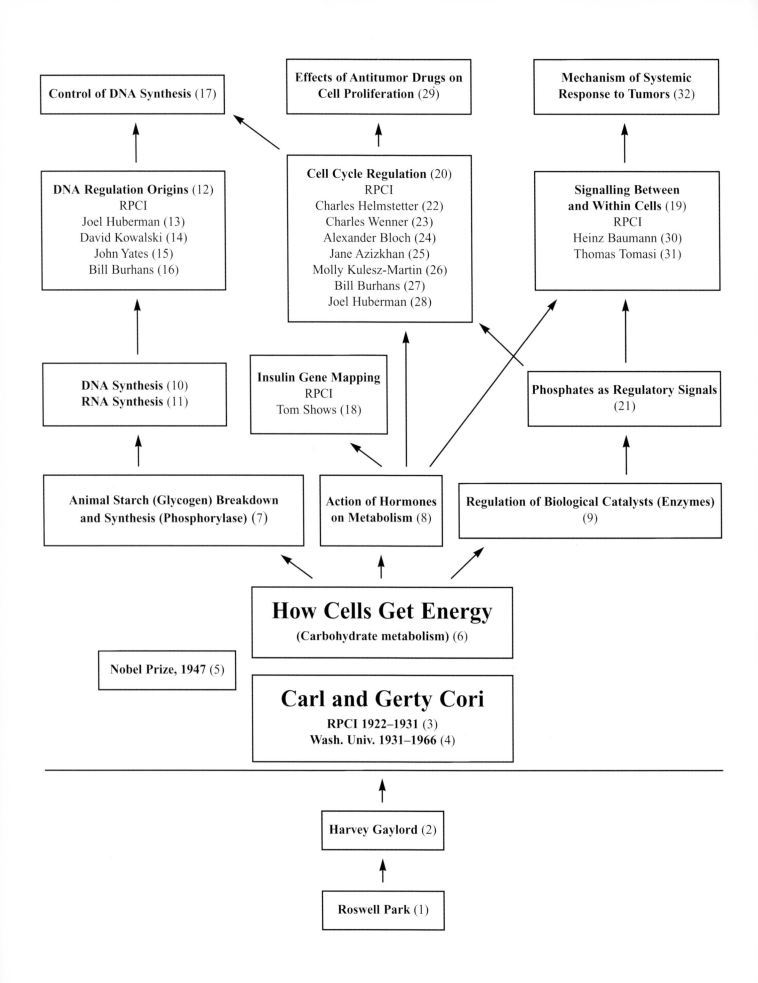

Control of DNA Synthesis (17)

Effects of Antitumor Drugs on Cell Proliferation (29)

Mechanism of Systemic Response to Tumors (32)

**DNA Regulation Origins** (12)
RPCI
Joel Huberman (13)
David Kowalski (14)
John Yates (15)
Bill Burhans (16)

**Cell Cycle Regulation** (20)
RPCI
Charles Helmstetter (22)
Charles Wenner (23)
Alexander Bloch (24)
Jane Azizkhan (25)
Molly Kulesz-Martin (26)
Bill Burhans (27)
Joel Huberman (28)

**Signalling Between and Within Cells** (19)
RPCI
Heinz Baumann (30)
Thomas Tomasi (31)

**DNA Synthesis** (10)
**RNA Synthesis** (11)

**Insulin Gene Mapping**
RPCI
Tom Shows (18)

**Phosphates as Regulatory Signals** (21)

**Animal Starch (Glycogen) Breakdown and Synthesis (Phosphorylase)** (7)

**Action of Hormones on Metabolism** (8)

**Regulation of Biological Catalysts (Enzymes)** (9)

# How Cells Get Energy

(Carbohydrate metabolism) (6)

**Nobel Prize, 1947** (5)

# Carl and Gerty Cori

**RPCI 1922–1931** (3)
**Wash. Univ. 1931–1966** (4)

**Harvey Gaylord** (2)

**Roswell Park** (1)

**1897** Dr. Roswell Park and Edward H. Butler, Sr., founder and publisher of the BUFFALO EVENING NEWS, asked the New York State Legislature to introduce a bill providing a $10,000 grant to establish a cancer laboratory within the University of Buffalo School of Medicine. The bill passed in 1898, and the New York State Pathological Laboratory of the University of Buffalo became the first facility in the world dedicated exclusively to cancer research and the first historic reference to direct government support for cancer research. This laboratory has evolved into Roswell Park Cancer Institute. (Chapter 606, 1449, 1898)

**1900** Mrs. William H. Gratwick donated most of the funding for the construction of the Gratwick Research Laboratory which was completed in 1901, providing new quarters for the Institute.

**1903** Dr. Leo Loeb carried out seminal research on the genetics of transplantable tumors in rats.

**1904** Drs. Harvey R. Gaylord, George H. A. Clowes and F. W. Baeslack reported the first observations implicating immunological reactions with malignancy.

Dr. Clowes began extensive studies on the effects of chemicals and drugs on tumors, establishing the concept of chemotherapy to inhibit cancer growth and the first cancer chemotherapy program in the United States.

**1907** Dr. Clowes reported the effects of physical and chemical agents on carcinoma and the conditions under which immunity against cancer may be permanently induced in mice.

Dr. Gaylord reported on the parasitic theory of cancer causation.

Drs. Gaylord and Clowes participated in organizational meetings of the American Association for Cancer Research (AACR) May 7–8. The charter members also hosted the 1908 national meeting of the AACR in Buffalo.

**1910** President William H. Taft visited the Gratwick Research Laboratory, and later urged the creation of a federal cancer program modeled after the Institute.

**1911** The Institute became a State institution (Chapter 128, 1911), The New York State Institute for the Study of Malignant Diseases.

In 1911 and 1912 preparation and early study of vaccines, the search for parasites as possible cause(s) of cancer, transplantation studies of mouse and fish tumors and investigation of immune reactions to cancer continued to receive attention worldwide.

**1913** The New York State Department of Health announced that Dr. Burton Simpson had established a program at the Institute which offered free microscopic examination of specimens submitted by physicians statewide for the diagnosis of cancer. This model had a great impact on cancer diagnosis and was adopted by other states.

Cary Pavilion, a thirty-bed hospital, was constructed in which laboratory findings could be given immediate clinical application in a specialized, comprehensive setting.

From 1913 to 1931, Millard C. Marsh established an inbred strain of mice, the Marsh Strain. These mice were distributed worldwide.

**1914** Through the generosity of Mrs. Ansley Wilcox, who was treated for breast cancer by Dr. Park, the Institute received funds to purchase radium to treat cancers of the cervix, tongue, prostate and skin, making it one of the first centers to treat cancer using radium.

**1921** The first 200,000-volt x-ray machine was installed.

**1927** January 1, Roswell Park Cancer Institute came under the jurisdiction of the New York State Department of Health. (Chapter 48, April 18, 1926)

**1928** Drs. Carl and Gerty Cori reported on the carbohydrate metabolism of tumor tissue, particularly the rate of glycolysis of tumor tissue. In 1947, they were awarded the Nobel Prize in medicine and physiology for this work. Dr. Gerty Cori was the first American woman and only the third woman in the world to receive the Nobel Prize. Their work influenced future research at the Institute and elsewhere on the regulation of normal and abnormal cells.

**1930** Governor Franklin D. Roosevelt asked the New York State Legislature to appropriate $300,000 to the Institute to purchase 5,737 milligrams of radium, and necessary containers and other apparatus for its operation and storage. This increased the amount of radium at the Institute to 7,774 milligrams, the largest amount available at any one place for cancer treatment and for experimentation. His interest in cancer research at the Institute carried over in his presidency, resulting in his signing of the National Cancer Act of 1937 which established the National Cancer Institute.

**1936** Drs. Bernard F. Schreiner and William H. Wehr reported on the five- and 10-year end results of treatment of gynecological cancers by irradiation. Their data were recognized worldwide as outstanding and dependable.

**1946** The name was changed from the New York State Institute for the Study of Malignant Diseases to Roswell Park Memorial Institute. (Chapter 369)

Dr. Louis C. Kress appointed Dr. Joseph G. Hoffman as the Institute's first Director of Cancer Research. Dr. Hoffman had worked on the Manhattan Project and was one of the first in the world to study the effects of atomic radiation on humans.

**1950** Dr. Morton Levin issued one of the first reports on the relation of tobacco and lung cancer, based on patient histories obtained by Roswell Park Cancer Institute between 1938 and 1950.

**1952** Dr. George E. Moore vigorously began to implement the postwar blueprint for facilities and programs at Roswell Park drafted by Dr. Herman E. Hilleboe, Commissioner of Health, establishing the modern foundation for Roswell Park Cancer Institute.

**1953** Dr. Robert Guthrie, early staff member, discovered the PKU Test for phenylketonuria, which is routinely used to test newborn babies.

In the early 1950s, the work of Drs. James Elam and Elwyn S. Brown and physiologist Werner K. Noel on mechanical ventilation and artificial respiration revolutionized the field of anesthesiology. They were also the first to describe the use of mouth-to-mouth respiration.

In the 1950s research teams headed by Drs. Edwin Mirand, James T. Grace, Jr., George Moore and Mr. David Mount confirmed the multispecies tumor-producing effect of polyoma virus, renewing worldwide interest in the role of viruses in carcinogenesis. Dr. Mirand also discovered the polycythemic strain of Friend virus, demonstrated its erythropoietin-like effect, and was the first to show that erythropoietin was a polypeptide which could be produced outside of the kidney. Today, erythropoietin is widely used clinically.

Dr. Avery Sandberg established the Clinical Cytogenetics Lab at Roswell Park, identified the XYY male and made initial contributions to solid tumor cytogenetics.

In 1953 Dr. Theodore Hauschka identified abnormal chromosomes in neoplasia and developed the widely-used HA (ICR) strain of mice. Drs. Hauschka and Edwin Mirand later developed this strain germfree as the ICR Swiss Strain later used in space research.

**1954** In 1954 Dr. David Pressman and colleagues pioneered studies using radiolabeled antibodies to localize tumors and gained worldwide recognition for research on the structural characterization of antibodies and application of antibodies to defining surface antigens, including those found on neoplastic cells.

**1955** The Roswell Park Graduate Division of the State University of New York at Buffalo was chartered through the efforts of Dr. George Moore. To date, the Division has awarded master's and doctoral degrees to over 1,400 graduate students. Dr. Edwin A. Mirand has been Dean of the Division for most of its history.

**1956** Dr. Donald P. Pinkel established the Department of Pediatrics and participated in the first multi-institutional group to study cancer (Acute Leukemia Group B).

In the 1950s and 1960s two tissue culture media were developed which have had enormous impact on biological and pharmacological cell research. Dr. George E. Moore and colleagues developed RPMI 1640. Dr. Maire Hakala provided the basis for HAT (Hypoxanthine, Aminopterin, Thymidine) which has been essential to studies in molecular biology and hybridoma technology for monoclonal antibody production.

In the 1950s and 1960s Dr. George E. Moore developed a cell plant center to grow human B-lymphoid cell lines, which was the model for centers in Japan and England. He used these cells as cellular therapy for malignancies — providing early support for the concept of adoptive immunotherapy.

1960    Dr. Enrico Mihich and associates demonstrated for the first time that certain anticancer drugs work with immunological defenses of the host to attain their curative effects.

1964    Dr. Elias Cohen started one of the nation's first three voluntary Plasmapheresis Donor Centers for blood platelet collection.

1965    The Center for Crystallographic Research opened to study arrangements of atoms in substances. The Center was the only one of its kind in the United States.

1967    Dr. David Harker and the staff of the Center for Crystallographic Research successfully determined the intricate molecular structure of ribonuclease, leading to the production of synthetic enzymes in other laboratories across the country.

Dr. Vahram Bakamjian developed the deltopectoral, or Bakamjian, flap to reconstruct head and neck areas following surgery. The Bakamjian Flap is used worldwide and is still considered state-of-the-art in reconstructive surgery.

Roswell Park became the site of the Regional Center for Maxillofacial Prosthetics, one of only nine such centers in the United States. Prostheses, artificial devices used to replace missing parts of the body, are custom designed to help rehabilitate cancer and trauma patients who have head and neck defects or injuries.

1970    Between the early 1970s and late 1980s Dr. Thomas B. Shows made major contributions to mapping over 500 human genes associated with disease, established the system of human gene nomenclature, initiated the physical map for human chromosome 11, established the Department of Human Genetics, and co-chaired the committee responsible for the international registry of human genes, which is headquartered at Roswell Park.

In the early 1970s Dr. Edmund Klein first developed a protocol for the application of a highly effective topical anticancer agent, 5-Fluorouracil (5-FU), for skin cancer.

1971    Dr. Gerald P. Murphy invited a U.S. Congressional Committee chaired by Representative Paul Rogers to conduct a public hearing to promote passage of the National Cancer Act of 1971. Institute staff members were very much involved in the passing of the Act, resulting in President Richard M. Nixon appointing Dr. Murphy to the first National Cancer Advisory Board.

1972    Photodynamic Therapy, a laser/chemical treatment, was pioneered by Dr. Thomas J. Dougherty. PDT is used worldwide—as an investigational therapy—to treat cancers of the skin, breast, lung, bladder, esophagus and head and neck. In 1994, the U.S. Food & Drug Administration lifted PDT's investigational status and approved it as a standard for treatment of advanced esophageal cancer.

Mr. Cyril T. Garvey, of the Garvey Foundation, whose 13-year-old son Kevin died of cancer, purchased a house one block from the Institute to provide low-cost housing for patients and their families. Kevin Guest House, owned and operated by volunteers, is the oldest hospitality house in the United States and the prototype for Ronald McDonald Houses.

1973    Roswell Park marked seventy-five years of pioneering cancer research, treatment and education. The milestone was celebrated by over 900 people on May 2.

Dr. Edwin A. Mirand established CAN-DIAL, a statewide telephone information service on cancer. The National Cancer Institute used this system as a model for developing the nationwide Cancer Information Service (CIS). CAN-DIAL was also the model for the New York State Department of Health AIDS Hotline.

The James T. Grace, Jr., Cancer Drug Center opened. The facility was and continues to be the only academic center in the United States which has the capability of taking drug development from its conceptual stages in the chemistry laboratory through testing of the compound in clinical trials.

**1975**  Drs. Lucius Sinks and Arnold Freeman were the first to use high doses of the drug methotrexate to treat pediatric leukemia patients. This treatment has improved survival rates for childhood leukemia worldwide.

In the mid-1970s Dr. T. Ming Chu and his associates characterized a human prostate-specific antigen—the most effective parameter in the measurement of prostate cancer. Their discovery also led to the development of the PSA test which is used in screening for the early detection of prostate cancer in the United States and abroad. This research was inspired by the National Prostatic Cancer Project headed by Dr. Gerald P. Murphy.

**1978**  The first Adolescent Unit in the United States opened to meet the special social, emotional and treatment needs of teenage cancer patients.

**1979**  A Cancer Prevention-Detection Center was established to identify individuals at high risk of developing cancer. Each year, the comprehensive examination is provided to thousands of asymptomatic individuals at no charge.

Roswell Park established the DES Screening Clinic (Gynecologic Oncology), and the Thyroid Screening Clinic (Medical Oncology).

**1980**  Dr. Maire Hakala pioneered the development of the drug combination 5-FU and leucovorin. Results of clinical trials with this chemotherapy indicate a significant improvement in the response rate of patients with colorectal cancer—from 15 percent to 45 percent.

**1981**  Dr. M. Steven Piver established an international registry of families who have had two or more first-degree relatives with ovarian cancer. The Gilda Radner Familial Ovarian Cancer Registry was the only registry of its kind in the United States.

**1983**  Dr. M. Steven Piver described, for the first time, the significant role of the drug hydroxyurea in enhancing the effects of radiation in patients with cervical cancer. Patients treated with radiation and hydroxyurea sustain five-year survival rates of 94 percent compared to 53 percent in patients receiving radiation and a placebo.

Dr. Dutzu Rosner provided first-time evidence that brain metastases in patients with breast cancer can be treated with systemic chemotherapy. This finding dispelled the widely held belief that standard chemotherapeutic drugs delivered through the blood would not penetrate the blood-brain barrier.

Drs. Julius Horosewicz, Susan Leong and Edwin Mirand developed a technique that increased the yield of highly purified human beta interferon. The American Cancer Society asked the Institute to manufacture interferon for distribution to scientists across the nation. This was the only highly effective human beta interferon available at this time and was distributed worldwide for human studies.

Researchers participated in national studies which demonstrated that human beta interferon treatment significantly reduced the frequency and severity of exacerbations of multiple sclerosis.

**1984**  Scientists determined the structure of nicotinomide adenine dinucleotide (NAD), considered to be the singlemost important co-enzyme because of its involvement in dehydroxygenase reactions. Crystallographers had been attempting to determine NAD's structure for more than two decades.

Drs. Kailash Chadha and Eugene Sulkowski introduced and patented a new method of producing and purifying human leukocyte interferon on a large scale.

**1985**  A new Phillips Mammography Unit—the first of its kind in Western New York—was installed.

Physicians at the Institute conducted the nation's first clinical trials on tumor necrosis factor.

Based on technology developed at Roswell Park, the first computer-controlled laser for photodynamic therapy was manufactured and marketed by a Japanese firm.

**1986**  The Department of Dermatology began testing isotretinoin, a vitamin-A derivative, as a way to prevent skin cancer. Roswell Park was one of only eight centers participating in the national study.

Roswell Park was designated one of eleven centers in North America to participate in one of the largest antismoking studies ever funded by the National Cancer Institute. Roswell Park's portion of the eight-year *community intervention trial* (COMMIT), under the direction of Dr. K. Michael Cummings, explored whether a community-based antismoking campaign could significantly decrease cigarette smoking.

Drs. Lemuel Herrera, Surabhi Kakati, Zenon Gibas and Avery Sandberg played an instrumental role in determining that the genetic defect for familial adenomatous polyposis of the colon—a pre-malignant condition leading to colorectal cancer—was the result of a gene mutation on chromosome 5. Future studies in this area would lead to the development of a blood test to identify individuals at risk for colorectal cancer. Dr. Anne Marie Block is currently studying further cytogenetic relationships.

**1987**   The Long-term Follow-up Clinic was established under the direction of Dr. Daniel Green to provide specialized medical care, support and counseling to long-term survivors of childhood cancer.

Dr. Carl Porter found a link between polyamines, a chemical substance found in high concentrations in human semen, and the development and growth of certain types of cancer. Dr. Porter heads a national program investigating the role of polyamines in cancer cell proliferation and their potential as target sites in cancer chemotherapy.

Successes in lung cancer vaccine trials conducted and reported by researchers from George Washington University, Roswell Park Cancer Institute, Ottawa University and Allegheny General Hospital raised hopes for the future of immunotherapy. Five-year survival rates in 234 lung cancer patients who participated in trials involving a specific tumor-associated antigen (TAA) showed a 20 percent survival advantage for vaccinated patients over controls.

**1989**   The Health Express, a 34-foot mobile educational unit, began traveling to communities to bring breast cancer education and detection services to minority and medically underserved women.

A new state-of-the-art Mammography Center opened, under the direction of Dr. Paul Stomper.

The Division of Medicine was invited to participate in a national chemoprevention trial as part of the National Cancer Institute's burgeoning efforts to develop drugs to prevent or arrest cancer development.

In the mid-1980's, the Department of Surgical Oncology reported one of the country's lowest recurrence rates for rectal cancer (10 percent at five years); one of the highest survival rates for malignant melanoma (81 percent at five years); and new surgical techniques which enabled Roswell Park to achieve one of the best limb-sparing surgical rates in the country.

In the mid-1980's, through their pioneering use of a radiation implant following hysterectomy, Dr. M. Steven Piver and colleagues achieved among the highest cure rates in the country for uterine cancer. Dr. Piver also reported average survival rates for patients with advanced ovarian cancer which were among the highest.

**1988**   Dr. Carleton C. Stewart joined the staff to establish a Flow Cytometry Facility. Roswell Park has become one of the leading centers in the use of this highly sophisticated, highly sensitive diagnostic tool.

**1990**   Roswell Park was among the first three cancer centers approved by the National Cancer Advisory Board as a National Cancer Institute-designated Comprehensive Cancer Center through a new competitive review process implemented in January.

**1991**   A Chemotherapy Clinic was opened for adult outpatients. The Clinic has a pharmacy to allow on-site drug admixture and preparation of medications, as well as participation in patient education activities presented by a multidisciplinary team.

The Ambulatory Surgical Center was expanded to improve the efficiency of surgical care and the level of comfort of patients and their families.

The Division of Radiation Medicine successfully performed Western New York's first stereotactic surgery on a patient with a recurrent malignant brain tumor.

A human tissue repository for multiple sclerosis and neuroimmunologic research—the only one of its kind in the eastern U.S.—was dedicated.

The Bone Marrow Transplant Program moved into a new state-of-the-art unit.

Dermatologists began using photopheresis to treat cutaneous T-cell lymphoma, a debilitating and potentially fatal malignancy of the white blood cells. Roswell Park is one of the few facilities to offer this safe, effective procedure which has been approved as the standard therapy for the advanced form of this disease.

The founding of the Roswell Park Alliance by Anne and Donna Gioia and later the Roswell Park Alliance Foundation resulted in substantial contributions to the Institute from their activities.

**1992** The Division of Radiation Medicine successfully treated its first patient with high-dose brachytherapy, a rapid, more efficient way of delivering radiation directly to tumors. A Clinac 600C Radiotherapy Linear Accelerator—the first of its kind in Buffalo—was installed.

Roswell Park participated in the National Cancer Institute's tamoxifen trial, the largest breast cancer prevention study ever undertaken in United States history.

An effort initiated by Dr. Thomas B. Tomasi succeeded in obtaining authorization by Governor Mario M. Cuomo and the New York State Legislature of a $241.5 million Major Modernization Project for a new Roswell Park campus. The institute's name changed to Roswell Park Cancer Institute.

**1993** Western New York's first physician-monitored Nicotine Dependence Clinic opened. This program was aimed at heavy smokers who were physically and emotionally addicted to nicotine, and was one of the first in the nation to offer the nicotine patch as an aid to smoking cessation.

Dr. Pieter de Jong established human genome libraries that will be used to generate the first sequence of the human genome.

Dr. Hector Nava was the first clinician to publish work demonstrating the importance of total colonoscopy in patients with colorectal cancer.

A 600-hertz nuclear magnetic resonance (NMR) spectrometer was installed. One of only twenty such instruments in the country, the Bruker AMX 600 enables researchers to obtain the highest sensitivity available for structural studies in NMR.

The Department of Molecular Immunology reported arresting the growth of human lung tumor xenograft in severe immunodeficient (SCID) mice by administering a long-circulating liposome formulation of the drug doxorubicin. This was the first direct evidence that anticancer drugs delivered in this way are more effective in halting the growth of human tumors than more conventional delivery systems.

Reconstructive surgeons brought special microscopes into the operating room to microsurgically repair or connect intricate structures too risky to trust to the naked eye. Microsurgery improves the quality of life for cancer patients by reducing the number of operations and shortening post-surgical rehabilitation time.

The Brain Tumor Treatment Center was established in collaboration with the State University of New York at Buffalo, Millard Fillmore Hospital and Buffalo General Hospital to provide comprehensive treatment of all types of brain and spinal cord tumors in one centralized location in Western New York.

The Family Cancer Syndrome Registry was established by the Division of Surgical Oncology to track families that carry the gene for hereditary nonpolyposis colon cancer. The registry identifies families in which at least three members within two generations have had colorectal cancer, with one member diagnosed before the age of fifty.

A Department of Orthopedic Surgery was established within the Division of Surgical Oncology to bolster the Institute's ability to deal with bone tumors and related orthopedic problems.

The Bone Marrow Transplant Program was certified by the National Marrow Donor Program as both a Transplant and Collection service. As such, Roswell Park gained access to more than 900,000 potential donors, and is able to serve as a regional referral center for harvesting the bone marrow of donors. Patients, who need bone marrow transplants, but who do not have compatible, related donors, will not have to leave Western New York for treatment.

The Division of Radiation Medicine acquired a Clinac 2100 Radiotherapy Linear Accelerator for stereotactic radiosurgery. This unit has two high-energy beams (6, 18 MeV), five electron energies (6, 9, 12, 16, 20 MeV), and features a radiation source that can be rotated 360 degrees for treating patients.

**1994** The Department of Cancer Control and Epidemiology served as the coordinating center for the National Prostate Cancer Detection Project, the largest multi-institutional study to date on methods of early prostate cancer detection. Results from this study added to the mounting evidence that the use of ultrasound and the prostate-specific antigen blood test in conjunction with the digital rectal exam can significantly increase the detection rate for one of the most common types of cancer.

An international team of researchers, including members of the Division of Medicine, identified unique cells that cause acute myeloid leukemia. This discovery may one day lead to the development of more effective strategies to treat this common form of adult leukemia.

DNA samples from families registered in the Gilda Radner Familial Ovarian Cancer Registry were used for research on the BRCA1 gene— the gene which has been linked to familial breast cancer and ovarian cancer. Dr. M. Steven Piver co-authored the first paper that documented a link to BRCA1 in families with hereditary ovarian cancer in which there were three or more close relatives with ovarian cancer, but no cases of breast cancer in these families before the age of fifty.

Roswell Park investigators began participating in the National Cancer Institute-sponsored Prostate Cancer Prevention Trial to test the effectiveness of the drug finasteride in preventing prostate cancer. Eighteen thousand men at 222 sites throughout the United States are expected to enroll.

After a long association with the local Hospice, Roswell Park opened its first hospice inpatient unit to meet the special needs of patients with life-limiting illness.

**1995** Roswell Park researchers found fibers of cigarette filters in the cancerous lungs of smokers, suggesting that filters may actually contribute to, rather than prevent, the development of lung disease and cancer. Dr. John L. Pauly and colleagues reported that there is probable cause to suggest that cellulose acetate filter fibers are inhaled or ingested, and may become lodged indefinitely in the lung tissue of longtime smokers.

Researchers from the Biomathematics Resource Facility designed a computer which accurately and objectively records and analyzes data for tumor growth.

A multidisciplinary Lymphedema Treatment Service was established.

A medical team of physicians, radiologists and nurses began offering cryosurgery, a surgical procedure which uses liquid nitrogen to freeze tumors of prostate cancer patients who could not tolerate conventional therapy.

The Center for HIV-related Malignancies was established to meet the special needs of patients who have cancer as a result of human immuno-deficiency virus infection. Offering unique, cutting-edge therapies, several of which have been pioneered at Roswell Park, the Center was designated an AIDS Treatment Center by the New York State Health Department in 1996, making it the only such center in the State to exclusively treat AIDS-related cancers.

The U.S. Food and Drug Administration approved the drug Photofrin, developed by Dr. Thomas Dougherty—as a palliative treatment for patients with obstructing esophageal cancers. This was the first photodynamic therapy drug approved in the United States. Also, in January 1998 the FDA gave approval for the use of Photofrin in photodynamic therapy to treat patients who have early-stage lung disease.

Research explored the seemingly unlimited possibilities of delivering effective vaccines for Hepatitis-B virus, the leading cause of liver cancer, in genetically-engineered foods. Dr. Yasmin Thanavala determined that genetically-engineered foods, such as bananas and potatoes, may replace traditional fermentation systems to produce vaccines.

The Division of Radiation Medicine acquired a Therapax HF 150 Contact Therapy Unit, the first of its kind in Buffalo, to spare patients who have easily accessible tumors the discomfort of surgery in favor of a simpler, less invasive radiation procedure.

**1996** The Clinical Genetics Service, one of the first to be established at a comprehensive cancer center, was established to provide women at high risk for breast cancer with counseling, instruction and gene testing, if desired. In 1996, Roswell Park began to offer genetic testing to women at high risk for developing breast and ovarian cancer. Under a clinical research protocol, the BRCA1 test is available to women who have been diagnosed with breast cancer and have a family history of breast and/or ovarian cancer, or are a relative of a BRCA1 carrier.

In response to the recent isolation of the breast cancer susceptibility gene, Roswell Park established the first Breast Cancer Registry in Western New York for women with a strong family history of the disease.

Researchers in the Division of Medicine began testing a promising new vaccine against pancreatic cancer, a silent, virulent disease which has one of cancer's poorest survival rates.

A renewed interest in cryosurgery at Roswell Park translated into a viable therapeutic option for patients with primary and secondary liver cancers. In an effort to improve the dismal prognoses associated with these cancers, the Division of Surgical Oncology established the Hepatic Cryosurgery Center.

Garth Anderson and Morton S. Kahlenberg published a landmark study which cast doubt on the widely held belief that the mutation of the p53 gene triggers the chain reaction of cancer development. This research indicated that p53 is the last step in the process, not the first.

The Department of Dermatology opened the Pigmented Tumor Clinic to diagnose, treat and monitor benign tumors, such as moles, as well as potentially life-threatening skin tumors such as melanoma. The Clinic is designed to determine risk factors—including a genetic predisposition—to certain pigmented tumors and to establish standardized treatment guidelines.

**1997** Dr. David C. Hohn worked with Governor George E. Pataki, Commissioner of Health Barbara A. DeBuono, and State legislators to obtain new governance for Roswell Park, and on October 15, 1997, Governor Pataki signed a landmark bill authorizing the Institute to establish a public benefit corporation allowing for greater governance flexibility. Roswell Park Cancer Institute had been a facility of the New York State Department of Health since 1927.

**1998** The second Board of Trustees in the history of Roswell Park Cancer Institute met for the first time June 19, 1998.

Dr. David C. Hohn
Present President and CEO

## PAST INSTITUTE DIRECTORS

Dr. Roswell Park     Dr. Harvey R. Gaylord     Dr. Burton T. Simpson     Dr. William H. Wehr

Dr. Louis C. Kress     Dr. Morton L. Levin     Dr. George E. Moore     Dr. James T. Grace, Jr.

Dr. Gerald P. Murphy     Dr. John R. Wright     Dr. Thomas B. Tomasi     Mr. Gordon Hennessy

Dr. Louis C. Kress

Dr. William H. Wehr

Dr. James T. Grace, Jr.

Dr. Edwin A. Mirand

Dr. C. William Aungst

Dr. David Pressman

Dr. Fred Rosen

Dr. Enrico Mihich

Dr. Timothy O'Connor

Dr. Verne Chapman

Dr. James Karr

Dr. Youcef Rustum

Dr. Jerome Yates

Dr. Andrew Gage

Ms. C. Angela Bontempo

Hospital Administrators,
Business Officers and
Health Research Administrators
(Past and Present)

Mr. Arthur Lepinot

Mr. Robert Aungst

Mr. Frank Muddle

Mr. Robert Goehle

Mr. Michael Rodzenko

Mr. Gerald Schofield

Mr. Frank Guglielmo

Mr. Russell Ketcham

Dr. Robert Ausman

Mr. John Apostolakos

Mr. Michael DeLellis

Dr. J. Holland

Dr. E. Henderson

Dr. C. Bloomfield

Dr. L. Leichman

Dr. W. Regelson

Dr. R. Ellison

Dr. H.J. Wallace, Jr.

Dr. O. Selawry

Dr. T. Prentice

Dr. H.D. Preisler

Dr. P. Creaven

Dr. E. Levine

Dr. M. Czuczman

Dr. N. Christiansen

Dr. N. Meropol

Dr. M. Baer

Dr. T. Baker

Dr. S. Bernstein

Dr. Z. Bernstein

Dr. M. Caligiuri

Dr. B. Lipman

Dr. D. Raghavan

Dr. G. Herzig

Dr. P. McCarthy

Dr. K. Foon

Dr. A. Sandberg

Dr. J. Sokal

Dr. L. Stutzman

Dr. K. Shimaoka

Dr. J. Plager

Dr. S. Greenberg

Dr. M. Wetzler

Dr. E. Sarcione

Dr. E.D. Holyoke    Dr. N. Petrelli    Dr. R. Gerner    Dr. A. Watne    Dr. W. Meeker

Dr. A. Mittelman    Dr. G. Elias    Dr. H. Nava    Dr. J. Evans    Dr. C. Karakousis

Dr. J. Smith    Dr. M. Rodriguez-Bigas    Dr. W. Kraybill    Dr. T. Tsangaris    Dr. H. Douglass, Jr.

Dr. T. Dao    Dr. T. Nemoto    Dr. S. Edge    Dr. T. Hurd    Dr. J. Graham

Dr. J. Barlow    Dr. M.S. Piver    Dr. S. Lele    Dr. R. Hempling    Dr. F. Marchetta

Division of Pathology
(Past and Present)

Dr. J. Pickren

Dr. J. Gaeta

Dr. Y. Tsukada

Dr. J. Brooks

Mr. E. Burke

Dr. E. Sproul

Dr. L. Simpson

Dr. M. Barcos

Dr. U. Kim

Dr. E. Nava

Dr. R. Penetrante

Dr. E. Neter

Dr. G. Reynoso

Dr. J. Fitzpatrick

Dr. G. Collins

Dr. E. Jennings     Dr. Z. Grossman     Dr. P. Stomper     Dr. S. Herman

Dr. S. Laufgraben     Dr. W. Zimmer     Dr. W.T. Murphy     Dr. J.H. Webster

Dr. R. Johnson     Dr. K. Shin     Dr. A. Adams     Dr. C. Sibata

Dr. M. McAuley     Dr. M. Bender     Dr. S. Bakshi     Dr. M. Blau

# Clinical Departments
## (Past and Present)

Dr. D. Pinkel    Dr. J. Cortner    Dr. L. Sinks    Dr. A. Freeman    Dr. M. Brecher    Dr. D. Green

Dr. M. Grossi    Dr. C. Tebbi    Dr. J.O. Elam    Dr. J. Mostert    Dr. R.J. Trudnowski    Dr. M. Lema

Dr. E.S. Brown    Dr. G.H. Hobika    Dr. J. Rempel    Dr. M. Palmer    Dr. K. O'Leary    Dr. D. Myers

Dr. O. deLeon-Casasola    Dr. V. Jones    Dr. H. Traenkle    Dr. F. Urbach    Dr. E. Klein    Dr. O.A. Holtermann

Dr. F. Helm    Dr. A. Oseroff    Dr. H. Milgrom    Dr. H. Stoll, Jr.    Dr. B.D. Wilson    Dr. J. Phelan

Dr. H. Solomon    Dr. N. Schaaf    Dr. W. Carl    Dr. D. Casey    Dr. E. Bockstahler    Dr. B. Majeroni

# Directors of Nursing
## (Past and Present)

Miss Ethel Chandler

Miss Mary Crook

Mr. Charles Martin

Mrs. Eva Noles

Miss Patricia Burns

Mrs. Georgia Burnette

Miss Catherine Lyons

# Representative Staff Scientists
## (Past and Present)

Dr. T.S. Hauschka    Dr. E.A. Mirand    Dr. J. Ambrus    Dr. C. Ambrus    Dr. G. Markus    Dr. K. Paigen

Dr. C. Helmstetter    Dr. V. Chapman    Dr. R. Elliott    Dr. C. Wenner    Dr. R. Swank    Dr. L. Maquat

Dr. A. Kinniburgh    Dr. J. Black    Dr. D. Musser    Dr. T. Shows    Dr. P.J. deJong    Dr. C. Stewart

Dr. J. Saroff    Dr. D. Sinha    Dr. D. Harker    Dr. H. Box    Dr. J. Bello    Dr. R. Parthasarathy

Dr. J. Alderfer    Dr. F. Orsini    Dr. T. Dougherty    Dr. B. Henderson    Dr. J. Subjeck    Dr. E. Mihich

Dr. Y. Rustum    Dr. M. Laskowski    Dr. A. Bloch    Dr. R. Bernacki    Dr. W. Korytnyk    Dr. C. Ip

| | | | | | |
|---|---|---|---|---|---|
| Dr. D. Yohn | Dr. W. Carter | Dr. J. Huberman | Dr. W. Held | Dr. R. Hughes | Dr. M. Woodworth |
| Dr. E. Sulkowski | Dr. G. Anderson | Dr. H. Weinfeld | Dr. R. Slaunwhite | Dr. W. Greco | Dr. T.M. Chu |
| Dr. S. Harvey | Dr. J. Yates | Dr. M. Goldrosen | Dr. H. Kohler | Dr. G. Mayers | Dr. R. Bankert |
| Dr. J. Black | Dr. S. Evans | Dr. E. Repasky | Dr. Y. Thanavala | Dr. R. Priore | Dr. I.D. Bross |
| Dr. J. Vana | Dr. C. Mettlin | Dr. B.I.S. Srivastava | Dr. N. Roberson | Dr. K.M. Cummings | Dr. L. Weiss |
| Dr. S. Leong | Dr. P. Aplan | Dr. J. Pauly | Dr. B. Seon | Dr. A. Sood | Dr. J. Vaage |

Dr. R. Rein    Dr. S.W. Hui    Dr. R. Mazurchuk    Dr. S. Murphy    Dr. A.L. Kazim    Dr. L. Blumenson

Dr. H. Baumann    Dr. T. Beerman    Dr. W. Burhans    Dr. K. Chadha    Dr. K. Gross    Dr. D. Kowalski

Dr. K. Manly    Dr. E. Morgan    Dr. S. Pruitt    Dr. P. Soloway    Dr. J. Azizkhan    Dr. B. Dolnick

Dr. M. Ip    Dr. H. Gurtoo    Dr. M. Kulesz-Martin    Dr. J. McGuire    Dr. C. Porter    Dr. B. Munson

Dr. H. Slocum    Dr. J. Sufrin    Dr. P. Hohmann    Dr. K. Matta    Dr. DiCioccio    Dr. M. McGarry

# Service Departments
# (Past and Present)

G. Pabst  A. Hutchinson  G. Ablove  R. Case  W. Payne

R. Hall  D. Terrana  J. Harris  J. Wasiura  D. Smith

A. Gustafson  J. Maj  D. Engel  F. Valvo  E. Kaczmarek

K. Kern  R. Ipolito  A. Connell  R. Pitoniak  M. Coyne

K. Synor  Rev. E. Ulaszeski  Rabbi M. Goldberg  Rev. L. Bigler

# Educational Affairs Department (Past and Present)

Dean Edwin A. Mirand

Mr. Russell DiBartolo

Mr. Donald Robie

Dr. Frank Hanavan

Dr. Diane Cookfair

Dr. M. Justa Smith

Dr. Arthur Michalek

Dr. Susan Leong

1981

L to R: William Held, Kenneth Gross, Charles Morreal, James Zucali, Craig Johnson
Edwin Mirand, M. Justa Smith, Nelson Slack, Howard Allen, Ralph Bernacki

1983

L to R: Charles Morreal, Sara Schneider, Judith O'Malley, Robert Rycyna, Michael DeLellis,
Arthur Michalek, Craig Johnson, Edwin Mirand, Curtis Mettlin, Diane Cookfair, Margot Ip,
Mary Jane O'Connell, Mary Woodworth, Gabor Markus

Administration and Staff Celebrating
Dr. T. S. Hauschka's 60th Birthday,
September 21, 1968

Dr. T.S. Hauschka

Dr. K. Paigen, Mrs. Hauscha, Dr. G.E. Moore

Dr. R. Elliott, Dr. C. Wenner, Mrs. G. Moore

Dr. Hauschka, Dr. M. Bennett, Dr. & Mrs. G. Murphy

Dr. Hauschka with Dr. G.E. Moore & Dr. D. Pressman

# Institute's Staff and 25 Year Club
## Celebrating, November 5, 1997

# Fund-raising Activities of the Roswell Park Alliance

All Star Night
(Celebrating 100th Anniversary,
February 21, 1998)

# Index

213

# Dr. Edwin A. Mirand

Dr. Edwin A. Mirand is Emeritus Vice President for Educational Affairs at Roswell Park and Dean of the Roswell Park Graduate Division of State University of New York at Buffalo. Dr. Mirand has been associated with Roswell Park for over five decades and, prior to joining the staff, was associated with the Institute as a graduate student at the University of Buffalo. Dr. Mirand received his doctorate from Syracuse University. In addition to his Institute responsibilities, Dr. Mirand has been a leader in numerous national and international professional organizations, serving as Secretary-General of the Thirteenth International Cancer Congress of the UICC, Secretary-Treasurer of the Association of American Cancer Institutes, President of the Association of Gnotobiotics, liaison member of the National Cancer Advisory Board, Chairman and member of the UICC U.S.A. National Cancer Committee of the National Academy of Sciences, and member of the New York State AIDS Advisory Council.

He is the recipient of many awards and special honors, including Honorary Doctorate of Science Degrees from both Niagara University and D'Youville College, Outstanding Alumni Award in Science, College of Arts and Science, SUNY at Buffalo, the Distinguished Service Award in Science Educaton from the New York State Science Teachers Association, and Merit Award of the International Union Against Cancer, the Margaret H. Edwards Award, the William H. Wehr Award. Dr. Mirand is the author of over 500 publications in the fields of endocrinology, virology, and cancer education and editor of several books in his field. Dr. Mirand is currently Senior Advisor to the President and CEO, Dr. David Hohn.